Una Kroll is a d
England and a medical practitioner. She was a
nun for five years, and a married mission doctor
for a shorter period. She then spent twenty
years as a family doctor before moving to her
present work as a community health doctor
seven years ago.

In 1967 she joined the Southwark Ordination
Course as its first woman student. She was
made deaconess in 1970 and has enjoyed a rich
and varied ministry ever since. She is an Oblate
of the Society of the Sacred Cross, whose core
members live in enclosure at Tymawr Convent.

Una Kroll was happily married to a priest
who was twenty-three years her senior. His
early retirement was spent caring for their four
growing children, who are now all working in
caring professions. In his later years he was
able to help his wife to understand the needs of
older people, and much of this book is the fruit
of their joint discoveries about the joys and
problems of growing older. He died in 1987.

Una Kroll

GROWING OLDER

Collins
FOUNT PAPERBACKS

To the Sisters
of the Society of the Sacred Cross

First published in Great Britain
by Fount Paperbacks, London in 1988

Printed and bound in Great Britain by
William Collins Sons & Co Ltd, Glasgow

CONTENTS

Chapter Four
FINDING THE VICTORIES

ACKNOWLEDGEMENTS

I am deeply grateful for my husband's companionship and for his personal experience and reflections on the subject of Growing Older. His thinking underlies much of what I have said in the text.

I would like to thank the Sisters, Oblates, Associates and friends of the Society of the Sacred Cross at Tymawr Convent for the way in which they shared their experiences of, and thoughts about, growing older. The quotations to be found in the text are only a fraction of the wealth of help I was given. Other people's valued contributions have added flavour to the text.

I am grateful for permission from Ann Morrish to publish her poem. "After Ninety"; to Faber Press for permission to publish Jenny Joseph's poem, "Warning", © Jenny Joseph, from *Rose in the Afternoon*, Dent, 1974; to Darton, Longman & Todd for permission to use extracts from W. H. Vanstone's *The Stature of Waiting*; to Ruth Robinson and Collins Publishers for permission to use part of her circular letter about her husband's death; to Sybil Harton and Hodder & Stoughton for permission to quote from her monograph, *On Growing Old*.

I thank Betty Houghton for help given in the preparation of the text for publication, as well as for insights into the subject.

On Growing Older

A man is as old as he's feeling
a woman as old as she looks.[1]

I am not yet old, but I am growing older. Being a woman I look my age and begin to feel its gentle tug at my elbow when I want to run for a bus, race up a hill, climb a mountain, wear my children's clothes or apply for an interesting job I've recently seen advertised. Yes, then I know that I am growing older and that, if I live long enough, I shall one day become an old lady. That thought does not frighten me, but it is a challenge, for I want to "grow old with a good grace",[2] and "to settle when the time arrives, into a green and smiling age".[3] If I am to achieve these goals I will have to plan wisely, overcome some obstacles on the way, and adapt to the changes in myself as I begin to experience the inevitable diminishments that accompany increasing age.

Much of my own understanding about the joys and problems of ageing has come from the experience of having lived with a husband who was twenty-three years older than I, and who lived until his eighty-sixth year. We were married for thirty years.

When he reached retirement age Leo was not old. True, he knew that the time had come for him to leave the demanding routine of full-time employment, but he was still vigorous, alert, fully involved in nurturing and raising our children, and able to enjoy being alive. Sensible planning and his resourceful approach to growing older helped to extend that enjoyment into old age. At the same time I am well aware that some unanticipated problems brought real misery into my husband's life, and that certain difficulties he and I had to meet brought fear and sorrow into our home. We faced his diminishing strength, increasing infirmity and spiritual struggles together. We were strengthened and sustained by our Christian faith, though not always in the ways we had expected when we were younger.

Because of the difference in our ages we always knew that it was likely that Leo would die before I did. We helped each other to talk about the pain, which grew steadily and relentlessly worse as he approached his death. I count it a great privilege that we had time to prepare ourselves for the parting, that he was able to die at home, and that his mind remained alert until five minutes before his death.

Since then I have gone on learning. I have been greatly helped by my children and friends. Like thousands of other people who have to face old age without the companionship of a beloved partner, I sometimes worry about becoming a burden to my children when sickness or infirmity catch up with me and I can no longer live on my own as I now do. I want to remain independent for as long as possible, and hope that I can find the inner resources I will need to anticipate and adapt to some of the difficulties that may lie ahead.

I am fortunate in that much of my working life has been spent as a family doctor, which has meant that I have been able to learn about ageing, not only from my husband but also from people I have met through my work. Being a family doctor was a very rich experience, for it brought me into intimate contact with life and death among young and old alike. It has been contact with young people that has set the problems of ageing into their proper perspective, for as R. L. Stevenson put it so elegantly, "old and young we are all on our last cruise".[4] All life is a preparation for death.

Most of us do not die in infancy. Some of us will die in our youth or middle age, but the majority of people alive today will live to reach a ripe old age. The whole of life is a learning experience which begins when we are born, increases as we grow into childhood and young adult life, and should continue until we die. If we are fortunate we should find that "to grow old is to pass from passion to compassion",[5] that is to say that as one quality in our lives diminishes another grows to take its place.

It is not easy to define the meaning of growing older. When I see a six-month-old baby at a well-baby clinic I will generally comment about the child's growth. I find myself using words to parents which describe my observations about their children. I'll say things like, "She's a bonny baby: look how well she's

growing", or, "He hasn't grown as well as he should
have done; let's see if we can find a reason for that".
Later, as I watch children growing up I know how
pleased the parents are when I can reassure them that
one of their children is growing taller and putting on
weight satisfactorily. When, somewhere between six-
teen and twenty-five years of age, young people
become "grown up" I know that I am usually referring to the fact that they have stopped growing taller,
rather than to their girth or state of maturity. Most
people attain physical maturity when they stop growing taller, but few could be described as emotionally
or spiritually mature. Those kinds of maturity are
forged during the years of adult life as people adapt
to the circumstances of their individual lives.

Although — since height and certain other signs of
physical maturity, such as the size of sexual organs,
are measurable — it is relatively easy to say when
someone has "grown up", it is far harder to say when
a person, who is growing older throughout life, has
actually "grown old". The passage of time brings
about changes which are obvious to all: skin wrin-
kles; hair turns grey; teeth decay; menstrual periods
stop; male potency diminishes; sight grows dim;
hearing becomes harder. These changes happen to us
all if we live long enough, yet it is also true that all
these things happen to different people at different
rates: chronological age is no measure of real age.
Even Jacques in Shakespeare's perceptive comment
on the ages of man in *As you like it* does not define
when "the sixth age shifts into the lean and slippered

pantaloon",[6] nor does everyone come to the "last scene of all", that is, "second childishness and mere oblivion, sans teeth, sans eyes, sans taste, sans everything".[7]

We know that we may never reach that "last scene of all", but we may be forgiven if that stark picture makes us dread old age and so try to turn away from seeing ourselves, or those whom we love and care for, as old. The fact is, however, that in Western civilization many more people than ever before are growing older and will reach old age. We are confronted with hard reality. We belong to an ageing population. Statistically our life expectancy at birth is now sixty-nine years for a man and seventy-one years for a woman. Many of us who are alive today will live on until our ninetieth birthday or beyond.

It is this reality that produces one of the grimmest paradoxes of our own generation. It is a fact that most people in a country like Britain, for instance, now consider that old age does not really start before men and women reach their seventy-fifth year of life. Many people would prefer eighty as a starting point rather than seventy-five. Be that as it may, special provision for old people in Britain's National Health Service does not begin until you are over seventy in most parts of the country. Social Service guidelines are similar: on the south coast's "Costa geriatrica", for instance, no one will generally qualify for a home help until he or she has reached seventy-five years of age. Nevertheless, it is also a fact that women and men are often told that they are too old for employment when they are "over forty", that far more people alive today will find themselves "on the scrap heap" or "pensioned off" before they are sixty, and that many of us will find ourselves living on relatively small incomes for some thirty or forty years of our lives. Given this paradox, it is small wonder, perhaps, that many of us who find ourselves still employed when we are fifty are afraid to change our jobs, and that those who do not have paid employment at that age, or younger, feel aggrieved. "Growing older" in those circumstances is not a pleasure, because those who are still employed and those who are not are equally imprisoned by their age, although in different ways.

If you and I are to meet the challenge of our own ageing intelligently and creatively we need to be realistic. It is no use ignoring the problems which stem from the fact that we are having to grow older in a society which does not value middle age, and which does not yet make adequate provision for old age. Equally, however, we should not ignore the pleasures that can come to us as we grow older, both because of the delights that come with maturity and because of the satisfaction that comes from meeting and overcoming some of the problems and difficulties that are necessarily encountered if we live long enough to reach old age.

There is also another reality to face. We ought not to be thinking about "growing older" only in our own cultural context. People who are growing older in Britain face one set of problems, and these are shared with many people in other highly industrialized countries. Those who grow older in other parts of the world may face a different set of problems. Life expectancy in the Southern hemisphere, often referred to as the Third World countries, for instance, is far less than in the Northern hemisphere, often known as the First and Second World countries. People who live in the Southern hemisphere grow older, but very few will encounter the problems of extreme old age. The economic circumstances in many extended families living in the *favelas* of South America, the slums of African cities or the rural communities of India, are such that everyone, young and old, must contribute to the survival of the family. A "pensioned off" retirement, such as we have in most highly industrialized societies in the Northern hemisphere, is almost unknown in impoverished parts of the Southern hemisphere.

In many cultures other than our own attitudes towards old people are much more positive than they are in countries such as Britain. Have these differences in life style anything important to say to those of us who live in relatively affluent industrialized societies? Can we learn from other people's experience in different countries and cultures? Do we have anything at all to share with them? Having lived for reasonable lengths of time in two different African countries, I feel that I can answer all three questions affirmatively. In writing this book I have necessarily focused on the experience of living in a Western society, but I also know that we need to look at what we can learn from people who grow older in other areas of the world.

I have written this book with both the pleasures and the problems of growing older in mind. I am not romantic about old age. There are certain possibilities, such as toothlessness, physical helplessness and senility, which I dread. I have found that the only antidote for such fear is to cultivate a positive attitude towards growing older. I try to do this by looking at some of the pleasures that come with maturity. I have also tried to find practical ways of postponing the consequences of natural ageing, and of overcoming the inevitable difficulties that I can see on the horizon as I prepare for my own retirement.

In one way, then, this is a very personal and practical account of one person's experience of growing older within an ageing community. In another way, I could only write such a book because of my profound conviction that human beings are meant to go on growing throughout their lives, that there is no point at which we need, or should, stop, and that the spiritual challenges which we face as we grow older are more important than either the pleasures or pains of ageing. Death, our own death, is the second most important event of our existence. We had no choice about our birth, its conception, circumstance or manner. We could not prepare for it consciously. We have no choice, either, about our own death, unless we determine to commit suicide, and even then we know we may not succeed in carrying out our intention. We do, however, have the opportunity of preparing ourselves for death while we are still very much alive. Growing older offers us time to prepare. I feel I want to use some of that time to learn from other people and to share what I have learnt with those who are reading this book.

Does having a deep religious faith, as I have, help us to meet the spiritual challenges inherent in growing older and facing death? Not necessarily: indeed, it can make it harder, not easier, as I shall show. Religious faith, or, conversely, its positive rejection, is an important part of human experience and needs to be taken seriously by everyone, especially those whose faith is tested in the fire of suffering.

It is, I suppose, because I have spent most of my life as a practising doctor of medicine with people who are having to face problems or real suffering in their lives that I am more aware of the difficulties of growing older than of its pleasures. That is why I have found it necessary to make a conscious effort to look at the pleasures first, the problems second and the victories last. Throughout I shall travel hopefully because my hope is rooted in past and present experience. I have good reason to believe that the future holds out the promise of further insights into the mystery of life as we approach death.

1

The Pleasures of Growing Older

Introduction / New freedoms / New perspectives / The fruits of experience / Rewards and satisfactions / Anticipations

Preparation for old age may mean the adoption and the cultivation of a new mental and spiritual outlook which obviously must claim our attention long before the end, and the middle years are not too early to begin it.[1]

Introduction

When I was young enough to be a mother to growing children, we used to take our three daughters to the cathedral where our son was a chorister. We'd take him out to lunch and then, while he was at rehearsal for Evensong we'd wander round the precincts, gaze at the soaring pillars of the nave and fill in the time before Evensong by visiting the ecclesiastical bookshop which was discreetly placed just outside the cathedral itself. Although I wanted to see our son and enjoyed the lunch part of it, I also disliked those long Saturday afternoons, because the younger children often became bored and fractious as there was so little to do and nowhere to sit. We felt honour bound to end each visiting day by attending the choral service, during which, I must admit, I spent most of the time looking at the only boy I knew in the choir. In this way I watched seven years of his life pass, as he grew from a bemused apprentice into a head chorister. Those monthly visits to see our growing son are indelibly printed on my memory for another more poignant reason. During those seven years, when I saw our son and our other children growing up, I was also watching my clergyman husband growing old enough to become a senior citizen. The cathedral is the place where I learnt to accept that fact, and took on the task of being the wage-earner for our family.

One Saturday afternoon, just before the service had begun, I picked up one of those illuminated prayer cards which can be found in most cathedrals. This was the very well known one beginning:

> Lord, thou knowest better than I know myself that I am growing older. Keep me from getting too talkative, and thinking that I must say something on every subject and on every occasion. Release me from craving to straighten out everybody's affairs.[2]

I laughed, turned to Leo and said, "Anyway, this doesn't apply to you", for it was a family joke that he spoke little and never interfered in other people's affairs. As I said it I felt a stab of pain in my heart, for it was the first time that I'd acknowledged that he was growing older. Later, during the service, I took my eyes off the choir, looked at the man sitting by my side and saw for myself the marks of his age on his face and hands. It was a shock, one that I can remember to this day, for at the time I found nothing pleasurable in what I was seeing. Indeed, the only way I could counter the pain of that moment of truth was to go straight to a mirror when we finally got home and tell myself firmly that I too was growing older. So what?! So, truth compelled me to accept that my husband was now a pensioner, that I didn't like it, that I was afraid of the future, that I didn't know how I would react to his being old when I was still middle aged, that I would have to change my attitudes towards ageing if I was to help him to enjoy being older, or to have any chance myself of growing older gracefully.

I regard that particular Saturday afternoon as one of the turning points in my life. It is one for which I am deeply grateful: the truth set me free to explore new perspectives on ageing, new insights into life, new ways of growing into greater maturity, new ways of forming relationships. I emerged from these explorations with a deeper appreciation of the blessings of a stable marriage, and I also learnt to relate more sensitively to patients and friends who were of pensionable age or older. During the fifteen years since that day I have learnt, initially from other people, and, now that I am near to retirement myself, from my own experience, to adopt an attitude towards life that can blend the truth with a determination to enjoy what can be enjoyed, sidestep the problems that can be sidestepped and accept limitations where they cannot be avoided.

I do not now feel discouraged or depressed at the idea of growing older, and I have reaped the advantages of those "middle years" to which Harton refers. I have found that middle age is a good time to cultivate a new mental and spiritual outlook. Other people who have been able to do this have taught me that such an outlook can be a source of great strength when hard times come in later years.

New Freedoms

> I grow old . . . I grow old.
> I shall wear the bottoms of my trousers rolled.[3]

T. S. Eliot wrote those lines at a time when it was unfashionable for young men to wear the bottoms of their trousers turned up. Prufrock's expressed intention to "wear the bottoms of my trousers rolled" is a sign of an older person's freedom to disregard the whims of fashion that enslave younger men and women.

Young people often like to wear "the right gear" because it helps them to win the approval of the peer group to which they most want to belong. It is no accident that each younger generation develops its own distinctive style of clothes, its own characteristic rules of behaviour, musical tastes and cultural norms.

Young people's fashions and behaviour sometimes provoke adverse comment from the older generation, but they also help those who are young and relatively immature to find each other in friendship: they give many young people a feeling of solidarity with each other in an otherwise uncomfortable world. Later on, when the responsibilities of having to work for a living and maintain a home are beginning to bite, these same young people will generally find it necessary to conform to the norms of other sections of society, where wearing different "right clothes" and doing other right things socially can make the difference between the success or failure of one's ambitions.

When the middle years arrive, however, we begin to come to terms with our ambitions. We realize that certain things we hoped for when we were younger are not going to happen. It is then that we can begin to claim our freedom from the need to conform to behaviour which was appropriate in our youth.

Some people never claim that freedom because they cannot bring themselves to the point of acknowledging their age. It is quite easy, for instance, to find middle-aged men who demonstrate their pretence to youth by their displays of frenetic virility towards beautiful young women. It is equally easy to find middle-aged women inviting ridicule by wearing clothes that would grace younger bodies but do nothing at all for their scraggy necks and ageing skins. There are also plenty of people who refuse to make any concessions to increasing age at all, and who continue to play games and pursue physical activities in which they can no longer excel although they still expect to do so. Perhaps, if we are honest, there is a bit of a Peter Pan, the boy who never wanted to grow up, in all of us. Nevertheless, most of us eventually do manage to accept the fact that we are no longer young and are growing older all the time.

That acceptance starts for many of us on the day when we look at ourselves in the mirror and have to admit that our grey hairs are beginning to show. Our beauty is waning; we shall never win that competition we thought we should have won when we were seventeen. Once we have admitted to the more obvious physical changes in our bodies we can go on to accept other facts about ourselves. Our muscle power is beginning to decline; we shall never win that coveted tennis trophy or run a mile in less than four minutes. Either we will never have children, or our family is complete: we have reached the age when we are no longer able to bear children. Our age debars us from entry into some other cherished profession. Our spell of unemployment is such that it is most unlikely that we shall get a job before we reach retiring age. Our ceiling at work has been reached: we are no longer eligible for that next step up the ladder of promotion.

As the moment arrives when we can admit that certain ambitions are not going to be fulfilled, we are free to discover other more appropriate ambitions. Seizing this moment of freedom is crucial to successful maturity, for it is a door to other freedoms. It can be a marvellous feeling, for instance, to wake up one morning and find that you no longer need to "dress to kill", that is, to dress to attract a desired partner and to "destroy" your rivals, but can now dress to please yourself. This pleasure is anticipated in a spendidly expressive poem by Jenny Joseph:

When I am an old woman I shall wear purple
With a red hat which doesn't go,
    and doesn't suit me.
And I shall spend my pension on brandy and
    summer gloves
And satin sandals, and say we've no money
    for butter.
I shall sit down on the pavement
    when I am tired
And gobble up samples in shops
    and press alarm bells
And run my stick along the public railings
And make up for the sobriety of my youth.
I shall go out in my slippers in the rain
And pick the flowers in other people's
    gardens
And learn to spit.

You can wear terrible shirts
    and grow more fat
And eat three pounds of sausages at a go
Or only bread and pickle for a week
And hoard pens and pencils and beermats
    and things in boxes.

But now we must have clothes that keep us dry
And pay the rent and not swear in the street
And set a good example for the children.
We must have friends to dinner
   And read the papers.

But maybe I ought to practise a little now?
So people who know me are not too shocked
   and surprised
When suddenly I am old and start to wear
   purple.[4]

I feel that I know exactly what she means. I have now reached the age when I can wear purple and psychedelic socks if I want to, even if I do look ridiculous to other people. Clothes become a true reflection of personality when you stop putting on clothes and attitudes to please others, and start using them to declare your individuality without fear of the consequences.

This freedom of choice comes when we stop trying to conform. Other opportunities come to us when we can admit that certain responsibilities have come to an end because of our age. When that happens we shall find that we can begin to do things that we have always wanted to do but had to put off when we were younger because we were so busy at that time. This is especially true for those of us who have been parents. The years between the end of child-bearing and the different responsibilities of being grandparents can be precious. A couple can begin to go on holiday together, unencumbered by their children's needs, demands and temperamental quirks. They can enjoy sexual intercourse without fear of being interrupted by their youngest child's sudden need for a drink of water in the middle of the night. If the woman has reached her menopause they can make love without fear of an unwanted pregnancy. When the children have grown up and left home a couple can discover the pleasures of being alone with each other in a home that can be kept relatively tidy for the first time since their eldest child was born. Parents can often begin to enjoy the kind of friendship with their adult children that was denied to them during those children's formative years. Although many parents do not have a long period of freedom from financial responsibility for their offspring before their natural desire to help their grandchildren begins to make demands on their pockets, it is the freedom from direct responsibility for a child's welfare that is precious and so enjoyable if only it can be claimed without hesitancy or undue guilt.

The freedom of the middle years of life is somewhat different for single people and those who remain childless by choice. Many men and women remain single because they feel that this is how they want to live their lives. When a woman reaches the menopause, and knows for certain that she will never bear a child, she can experience real relief that the choice she has had to exercise throughout her fertile years has been completed by nature and is now no longer a matter of choice but of fact. Many nuns have told me of their sense of fulfilment when that moment has come for them and they know that their offering to God has been ratified for ever. Those who have such a vocation to celibacy do not experience regret at their childlessness: they are released from the ties of home and children in order to serve God and their neighbour in ways that would be impossible were they to be married. The same relief comes to any woman who has chosen not to have children, either because she feels she should not have children, or because she feels that the nature of her work is incompatible with motherhood. Men do not have the same definite end to their fertility, but married men who agree with their partners that they will not have children, and those who remain single from choice, can also claim the benefits of their decision if they have a mind to and have a vocation not to enter a partnership that can lead to parenthood.

This freedom from child-bearing and rearing that comes to most of us in our middle years of life is not always a blessing, of course, nor can it be claimed by everyone. There are men and women who become embittered because of their childlessness: their years of growing older are marred by their infertility. There are parents whose children can never leave home, perhaps for some mental or physical handicap, perhaps for some other reason. There are many women of post-menopausal age who have to rear other people's children because of the death of a relative or because their chosen work is to be a foster parent to orphans or children in the care of the local social services. I know all this, but I have chosen to speak of these years of relative freedom from the responsibilities of parenthood because I feel that many more people could enjoy these years if only they would allow themselves to do so: they are years of opportunity we have a right to claim and enjoy.

When, in due course, the time comes to accept the unpalatable fact that we have reached the ceiling of our ambition as far as work goes, we often feel sorry for ourselves. I suggest that the disappointment, real as it is, can be a gateway to a new and much more pleasurable way of life. Ambition is a hard master. The struggle to win promotion, necessary as it may be to our self-esteem, will almost certainly involve the loss of some friendships, the cultivation of some attitudes that we secretly despise and the surrender of some principles we have cherished. We will probably know that we have obtained our own job, position and status at the expense of other people, who might be equally deserving but who have been on the losing end of the fierce competition within the office or group to which we belong. Now our turn has come. We are the ones to fall off the promotion ladder. Our self-esteem takes a knock. Once we stop despising ourselves for apparent failure, we can begin to look in other directions for our satisfaction. It is possible to spend less time at the office, more at home. We can use the energy, formerly spent on all those necessary extra appearances at office functions, parties and vocational courses, in other ways.

I have seen people blossom in their middle years because they have accepted the fact that their status and earning capacity are going to remain relatively static until they retire. They manage their present job easily; they know where they stand in the pecking order; they can budget according to a known income; they no longer need to move house in order to take up a higher post. For the first time in their lives, perhaps, they find that they have time to pursue a new hobby or to take a course in a subject that they have been interested in before but left alone because it did not directly benefit them at work. Most people manage to compensate for the loss of promotion prospects, but it is not so easy to do that when one is unemployed.

Unemployment is an unmitigated disaster to those who are threatened with imminent redundancy or to those who have already lost their jobs. In a country like Britain, for instance, adult citizens are expected to earn money through productive work for society. Workers are also expected to contribute, through taxation of various kinds, to the general welfare of those who do not work. Such expectations create a climate of opinion that is unfair to those who cannot work, for it induces a feeling of failure among many people who are not gainfully employed. Society itself might be ashamed that it cannot provide work for all its citizens, but such a burden of guilt should not be placed on unemployed people, whether they be young or old.

The disaster of unemployment is sometimes more

bearable when we are middle-aged or are approaching retirement age. Many people have told me that they are relatively happy to take early retirement in order to make way for a younger person who has never before had a chance of working. Alternatively, they have been quite pleased to cede their own post to a younger colleague, whose promotion has been blocked because senior people are no longer moving to other companies as they used to do in times of high employment.

If we can throw off some of the burden of guilt that society imposes on its so called "failures" we can often change disaster into success by using our increased freedom to choose to live in other ways, do other jobs or make new friends. Before I consider the new perspectives on life that we need to acquire in order to enjoy such situations, I want to consider the way in which some freedoms are lost altogether when we reach a certain age.

If we stop expecting to be promoted or become unemployed we can often hope to go on doing the kind of work we have done before, but our age puts an end to certain ambitions for ever. A woman of fifty-five, for instance, cannot expect to bear a child. Her freedom of choice has disappeared permanently. Similarly, in many professions there is an age ceiling for entry to training. Someone of thirty years of age could not expect to become a top class gymnast or acrobat, although they might still be lissom enough to enjoy the energetic physical exercise. Someone of sixty would not normally be admitted to a monastic order, because the physical and emotional rigours of a monastic novitiate are such that most people of that age would be unable to adapt themselves to such a different way of life, even though they might want to try it.

Certain freedoms such as these disappear for ever. With them go the hopes and fantasies we often cherish during our younger years. At some time or another we shall find that we have stopped hoping that one day we will be able to throw up our job as a bank clerk, for instance, to become a great opera singer, or win fame as a beauty queen. We have stopped looking for the ideal mate and have begun to appreciate our existing partner. We have stopped longing for the children we will never have.

This acceptance of the disappearance of certain freedoms can be liberating. We no longer need to look over our shoulders at what other people can do, or are doing, but can be content with our own circumstances, roles or partners. We settle for what we have accomplished, and no longer need to play games with ourselves about "what we might have been if only . . ." Moreover, there are times when we could quite legitimately claim a freedom but do not do so because of our love and concern for other people if we did what we could do. I have known people refrain from taking a new job or seeking promotion because it would interfere with the children's education or family life. The mature acceptance of such involuntary and voluntary restrictions on one's freedom of choice can open the way for the kind of settled contentment that makes life pleasurable. It is then that it becomes possible to find happiness in growing older.

I do not pretend that it is easy to give up our fantasies about our freedom to make choices. Many of the pains of growing older stem from people's inability to accept the disappearance of certain freedoms, as will be seen later on in this book. I do, however, think it is important to come to this acceptance of reality at the right moment of our lives if we are to enjoy growing older. It is easier to do this if we take stock of our perspectives on the purpose of life.

New Perspectives

> Grow old along with me
> The best is yet to be,
> The last of life, for which
>   the first was made;
> Our times are in his hand
> Who saith, "A whole I planned,
> Youth shows but half: trust God:
>   see all, be not afraid".[5]

During middle age people often come to a crisis point of dissatisfaction with the way in which they have lived their lives so far. This crisis may be forced on them by sudden illness, redundancy or the unexpected departure of a spouse or partner. It may be of their own making, because they realize that they have spent half, or more than half, their lives doing work they originally thought they would always enjoy but now find boring or frustrating. The crisis may happen because they have to admit to themselves that they have made a disastrous mistake in their choice of partner, or perhaps realize that they should never have married in the first place. These kinds of crisis are not always recognizable, but if they are, they can sometimes prove to be a turning point in people's lives.

I remember Ron, a friend who had joined the Royal Air Force as a young man. Initially he had done well and he reached the rank of Wing Commander. There he stopped. When he realized that he wasn't going to go any higher he decided to leave the Air Force and do something completely different. He had a reasonable pension, a desire to enjoy life to the full, and a good sense of humour. These were considerable assets.

My friend and his family emigrated to another country. Ron started a new life as a civilian without an ambition to make a spectacular success of his next job, but with a real desire to give good measure for his wages. He and his wife, Margaret, both found employment, and went on working until their children were grown up. Then they sold up their home, bought a motorized caravan, and took off on a prolonged exploration of the country they had chosen to adopt as their own. They spent several years exploring new areas of the country in this way.

Every so often they would stop somewhere for several months, pick up casual work as gardeners and handymen to supplement their fixed income, and then, when they felt like it, move on again in their mobile home.

At the time they were doing all this Ron and Margaret were both under retirement age. On the other hand I, who was close to them in age, was tethered to a responsible job as a family doctor. I was earning a high income and enjoying my job, but I did not feel free to do as I pleased. At one time I can remember feeling envious of them and rather critical too, even though I did not particularly feel that I wanted to follow their example. Those feelings changed when I met them again after several years and saw how content they had become with their chosen way of life, and also – and perhaps even more importantly – realized just how happy I was with my own life style.

Since then I have seen many people come to terms with apparent failure in similar ways. I have also seen some men and women change their jobs in midstream, because they have deliberately chosen to surrender their security for the prize of peace of mind and personal fulfilment. After years of struggle to stay in her chosen profession of medicine, Rita, another friend, decided that her emotional aptitude for the responsibilities of a medical practitioner did not match her intellectual ability to do the work. She abandoned medicine, became a marine biologist, and flourished. When I met her several years later she was a different person from the anxious, careworn doctor I had once worked alongside.

I now recognize that all three of my friends had used their years of maturity wisely. Ron had been forced by circumstances to make a choice between staying where he was, which he could have done without dishonour, or changing his way of life. Margaret had adapted herself to her new life and work. Rita had listened to an interior prompting which told her that she was emotionally unsuited to her chosen profession. She had shown considerable courage in making a change which other people did not find at all easy to understand.

I am not saying that all mid-life crises and changes have the kind of happy outcome I have been describing. I am simply suggesting that it is possible to use our years of maturity in these kinds of ways. I certainly feel that many people can grow older more happily when they find the courage to take the initiative and make the hard decisions that are sometimes necessary in such circumstances.

These kinds of decisions need to be taken in consultation with other people. It is always wise to test the temperature of the water before plunging into any new way of life. It is often possible to undertake new studies or to go on a course before making the change from one kind of work to another. Some of the happiest people I have met have been mature students on a three-year part-time theological course which I joined when I was over forty years old. Among my colleagues during those years were a bank manager, a business man, an advertising agent, an electrical engineer, a policeman, a power station operative, an insurance agent and a social worker. All of us retained our jobs and supported our families while we were training. One or two of the men dropped out during the first year of the course and continued with their original work, happy to discover that they did not want a change of any kind. The rest of us went on. At the end of the three years most of the men were ordained as clergymen in the Church of England. Some of them combined this new vocation with their original work. Others, in consultation with their families, decided to exchange their relatively high incomes and social status for stipendiary priesthood. It is now nearly twenty years since those decisions were taken, and my friends' happiness in their new roles has more than compensated for their changed financial status.

Older people have sometimes told me about the way in which an unexpected redundancy once provided them with the capital and the opportunity to choose a new career or to start up an independent business. Looking back on their lives they can be thankful for their misfortune, although they can clearly remember how disastrous it was at the time, and how difficult it was to regain the self-confidence to take up new employment or to launch out on their own. There must be great satisfaction in knowing that one has managed to overcome a crisis or disaster of that kind in one's own life. This can be a source of real pleasure to some older people.

Mid-life crises are not confined to our working lives. Many men and women find themselves having to face considerable unhappiness in their personal relationships. Marriages or partnerships may falter or fail. Choices about staying or leaving home have to be faced. Alternatively, some people face middle age with dismay, knowing that they have never found happiness with another person and will probably have to remain single and alone during their old age unless they take active steps to find a partner. Later on these men and women will feel either regretful or happy about the choices they have had to make at such times.

Many people make mistakes during their mid-life crises. Later they will have to bear the consequences of their choices. They may have cause, for instance, to regret that they left home, changed their jobs, sought a partner through a marriage bureau, or decided not to. Others, however, find that they made the right choices, and are deeply thankful that the crisis became a turning point in their lives.

Sometimes, perhaps most often, there is no crisis, no point at which definite decisions need to be made. Maturity brings its own happiness as the decades pass. Life is eventful, rich in opportunity and fulfilling, economically, domestically and socially. Even so it is wise to use our middle years, or pre-retirement phase to take stock, to look backwards and forwards at one and the same time. These are the years when we can still make choices. We can develop a talent we feel we have hitherto allowed to lie dormant. We might decide to learn to play the piano, learn a language, or take up some new hobby. Alternatively, we might decide to save up for a long-desired but hitherto unfulfilled pleasure such as going on a world tour, making a pilgrimage to the Holy Land or visiting our relatives in Australia or Canada. It is amazing to see how such a stock-taking exercise can give us the impetus to seize hold of opportunities to enjoy ourselves. When we do that we often find that we also give pleasure to others who are close to us, because we are usually easier to live with when we are engrossed in a new interest or working towards a "once in a lifetime" experience.

Whether our lives are relatively free from crises, or beset by them, growing older brings its own pleasure simply because we acquire experience which bears fruit in our lives.

The Fruits of Experience

"You are old, Father William,"
   The young man said,
"And your hair has become very white,
And yet you incessantly stand on your head –
Do you think, at your age, it is right?"

"In my youth", Father William replied
   to his son,
"I feared it might injure the brain;
But now that I'm perfectly sure I have none,
Why I do it again and again."[6]

Those verses by Lewis Carroll do my morale a lot of
good, because I'm aware that I do all sorts of things
in my mature years that I would have been afraid of
when I was younger. I wear the clothes I want to
wear rather than the ones I ought to wear as a
professional woman. I enjoy sitting on the floor when
younger colleagues think that I am old enough for
them to offer me the most upright easy-to-get-out-of
chair in the room. I do physical exercises that people
half my age think I'm crazy to attempt. It will, as I
very well know, all come to an end one day, when
real old age constrains my choice of clothes, restricts
my joint movements and tells me that it is no longer
wise to stand on my head. Meanwhile, however,
maturity and experience have released me from mere
conformity, and taught me what I can enjoy doing. I
have learnt about my limitations but have also understood how I can adapt to my changing age and
circumstances, and this applies to far more areas of
life than my appearance and physical prowess.

The years of maturity leading towards retirement
are often very pleasurable. By this time we should be
familiar with our work, even if we did take on a new
job or life style in middle age. We know how to
overcome some of the difficulties inherent in work:
we are not unduly disturbed when things go wrong;
we are still adaptable enough to find solutions to the
problems. We are also old enough to look back with
satisfaction to some achievements in our lives. It is
important that we claim this pleasure and do not fall
into the trap of denigrating ourselves. The self-

deprecation of a woman who says she is "only a housewife", or of the man who hangs his head when he tells you that he is "just a road-sweeper", needs to be discouraged. We should refute such attitudes and accept the fact that all work in the community, waged or unwaged, is valuable to society.

Our homes are an important area of our lives where we benefit from experience. By the time we can be described as growing older most of us will have been married, or lived with a partner of the same or opposite sex, for some years. We will have experience of making a home. We may have moved house once or twice. We will have begun to raise a family. We will know the quirks of our particular house, with its inadequate cupboard space, its awkward-to-clean cooker and its terrible draught in the main bedroom. More importantly, we will also have experience of the special strengths, weaknesses, likes and dislikes of our chosen partner, and we may be getting to know our children's personalities. By this time we will certainly know whether or not our partners are able to adapt to changes, enjoy the kinds of things we enjoy, and are willing to work with us, rather than against us, to find solutions to common problems. We will have discovered certain strengths and weaknesses in ourselves simply because we have chosen to live as we do, either alone, or with a partner, or in a group of other people. In the process of discovery most of us will have known occasional ecstasy, frequent delight and, best of all, found that we are capable of changes and growth.

I admit that in an unstable and highly mobile society, such as those which exist in countries like Britain, Canada and America, for instance, you have to be fortunate to find a settled way of life for sufficient time to allow yourself to enjoy the sense of achievement that comes to many when they have redesigned a house, or expanded an immature relationship into a more mature one. Nevertheless, stability does provide a source of happiness. For this reason people invest considerable energy in their personal relationships. They know what they want, and seek it actively. They are often prepared to work hard in order to find personal happiness.

In that search some people are greatly helped by the positive attitudes towards marriage and monogamy that exist within the Judaeo-Christian tradition. Others feel that undue emphasis on heterosexual "norms" of behaviour, and on fidelity as an essential ingredient of marriage, are responsible for a great deal of personal unhappiness among homosexuals and those whose marriages are breaking down for good reasons. The Christian community in particular needs to develop ways of helping everyone to enjoy stable relationships, rather than focusing only on those who are married.

One special pleasure comes to everyone who has formed a longstanding sexual partnership with another person. There is considerable joy in having sexual intercourse with someone so well known to you that you know exactly what gives both of you intense pleasure, yet so mysterious that there is always the possibility of a new discovery about him or her. The delight of discovering that one's pattern of sexual behaviour can change over the years, and even die out altogether, without substantially affecting the quality of the relationship is also great, but this pleasure can only be gained by those who are content to grow older together. Changes in any couple's intimate behaviour become part of their shared experience. The quality of their relationship is sometimes strengthened when the initial passion fades a little, or when it has to be restrained, as when, for instance, one partner becomes too ill to have full sexual intercourse but can still enjoy other ways of intimate cuddling and love-making. The strengths and weaknesses of each partner are exposed when any couple live with each other over a long period of time. They can learn the truth about themselves, so that they can change and adapt to each other's needs.

Those who have decided to remain alone, without a particular partner to share their home with, can also benefit from their chosen way of life. There are, indeed, pains in such a choice, and sometimes there are formidable problems, but some people are much happier on their own than they would be if their freedom and mobility were to be limited by the need to pay attention to the personality and career needs of a partner. They are in control of their own lives and feel satisfied.

What has been said about the pleasures of any longstanding partnership can also be said of lasting friendships. We may not see our friends for months or years, but when we do meet we start from where we left off, catch up and move forward at one and the same time. We may only make two or three friends of this kind during the whole of our lives, but they stand out in our memories like beacons whose flames warm us whenever we draw near and whose light illuminates our path as we leave each other to go our separate ways.

There are some friendships which are born quickly in adversity and are never, perhaps, renewed, but which last in one's memory. Writing in a book about the middle years of life, a Jesuit priest, Father Bernard Basset, told of the experience of a Polish priest who was imprisoned in Belsen during the 1939–45 War. The priest lived to tell of his experience:

> I was dying of dysentery and two fellow prisoners nursed me, saving their own pitiable rations to build up my strength. I had no possible way of repaying them, indeed I was expecting to die before morning, yet I had a glimpse of untold happiness at being loved simply for myself.[7]

That "glimpse of untold happiness" must, surely, have borne fruit in that priest's later years.

Whenever I think of people's perceptions about the experience of growing older I realize that it is impossible to generalize. Relationships and events which are pleasurable to one person may be painful to another. I, for instance, have enjoyed the challenge of overcoming fear ever since I was twelve years old, when I first stood on a ten metre high diving board and looked down at the water beneath me. I had gone up there as the result of a "dare". Standing there two fears gripped me, one of the fear of diving, the other the fear of having to climb down the ladder to my waiting friends. Diving off that board was both terrifying and exhilarating. Knowing that I could conquer fear in that way has stood me in good stead in other and different circumstances. It is, however, probable that I would have a different perception of that event in my life had I decided to take the sensible step of walking down the ladder. Other people, including my poor mother who was watching, did not find any pleasure in my action.

Each of us will have some crucial moments like that to look back on as we grow older. All of us, I believe, will have had significant pleasure at some achievement at some time. That in itself will give us personal satisfaction, but there are also other rewards that come to us in our mature years.

Rewards and Satisfactions

The first forty years of life give us the text;
The next thirty supply the commentary.[8]

As we grow older we begin to reap the rewards of our age. There is an old English proverb that says, "The older the fiddle, the sweeter the tune", and certainly that can be said about some longstanding family relationships, friendships and partnerships, although, even as I quote it, I am conscious that the length of duration of any relationship is not an indicator of its quality or success. The kinds of rewards and satisfactions I want to talk about now, however, do not depend on success at all, but are a simple consequence of being older, of having survived to reach middle age or old age.

Some of these rewards come through memories. Being older myself, my recall of past events is patchy, yet certain things stand out clearly, like that of being afraid on a high diving board, like some wartime memories which I can share with others of my generation, like certain tunes which play inside my head when I remember my youth. These kinds of rewards are universal. They are summed up in the words which Shakespeare put into Henry V's mouth when he spoke to his soldiers before the battle of Agincourt:

> He that shall live this day, and see
>   old age
> Will yearly on the vigil
>   feast his neighbours,
> And say, "Tomorrow is St Crispian".
> Then he will strip his sleeve
>   And show his scars,
> And say, "These wounds I had
>   on Crispian's day".
> Old men forget; yet all shall be forgot,
> But he'll remember, with advantages,
> What feats he did that day.[9]

One of my friends, who recently died at the age of eighty-six, was an old soldier. For over forty years he remembered his own wartime experiences on the one day a year when he went off to his regimental reunion. It was, he told me, a kind of pilgrimage into his past, and he kept it up until a year or two before he died. Talking to other old men after his funeral I understood, as I had not done before, why those reunions had been so important and satisfying to my friend, whose later years had been marked by gentleness and courage as he faced his last enemy alone, and without the companionship of his devoted wife, who had died before him.

Other rewards come to us from outside. These are often unexpected, for most of us do not feel as old as we are. The realization that we are older comes to us either from the looking glass, or, more usually – for we are adept at deceiving ourselves when we do look in the mirror – from other people who begin to treat us as we ourselves would expect to treat an older person. I can still remember the day when a younger colleague listened to my opinion with the kind of respect he felt he ought to show to someone who was "a bit long in the tooth". It wasn't the kind of respect you give a peer who has come up with a good idea. No, it was a slightly deferential humour that I saw in his eyes. I knew he would do as I suggested merely because I had the authority that he did not yet have at that stage of his career, but I also knew that I was growing older, indeed was old in his eyes. The moment passed and we talked as equals again; yet I knew and accepted the difference between us. The time had come for me to begin to settle into "a green and smiling age".[10]

Since that day I've learnt to enjoy "being my age", to value myself as a person of mature experience, to enjoy it when younger friends come and share their problems with someone whom they see as older and wiser than themselves, even if I don't often come up with a solution to their difficulties. I can even smile thankfully when I am offered the most comfortable chair in the room, even though I do not yet need to take advantage of such kindnesses.

My encounter with the younger doctor, and subsequently with others, has also taught me about another asset in being older, one that is increasingly important and pleasurable to me. I am no longer a rival to younger colleagues. I shall never get that consultancy they are chasing. I shall never have to apply for another job. If I were to be made redundant tomorrow I would be unemployable because I am so near to retirement age. I have found that knowledge liberating. My pre-retirement years have been free from the necessity of compromising in order to get a coveted "next post" which might "lead somewhere". There's nowhere to go, and even dismissal would not be a disaster. Within these limitations I am free to go on creating, innovating and making decisions. If the next few years stop being enjoyable I shall be content to retire earlier than I need do.

That freedom from rivalry at work is extended to my relationships with men and women outside my family. Friendships were enriching to our own marriage. Recently I have seen the fear disappear from other women's eyes, particularly those who are much younger than I, when they realize that I am no longer, and never again will be, a sexual rival. The quizzical frankness of a child who, looking at me hard and long, said, "You are old", I regard as a compliment as well as the truth as far as he was concerned. He knew instinctively that I would not be offended, and he was right. I have seen the same truth, though unspoken, relayed to me in the eyes of young women and men who honour me with their confidence and affection, and now, increasingly, I see it in the attitudes of my older friends. I suppose that this is a common experience among women who are growing older, although it seems to be less common among men whose middle years, as I have already said, are often marked by earnest attempts to endorse their virility by making sexual conquests of younger people. Many problems stem from such refusals to admit that one is growing older, and I shall be looking at some of these in a later section of this book (see pages 75–81 and 111–13. All I want to emphasize here is that it can be delightful as well as a relief to be able to enjoy friendships that are based upon mutual attraction, yet free from any need to pay sexual compliments to each other. A necessary precursor to such pleasure is the ability to see ourselves as we are seen by other people, and to accept with equanimity our grey hairs, wrinkled skins and other signs of ageing.

My own working years have been satisfying. It is now good to see our children and my younger professional colleagues taking over work that I shall soon be able to lay down. I have rich memories to sustain me in my old age. There is a sense in which I need no other reward or token of achievement, nor am I likely to receive any. Nevertheless, many people are rewarded and honoured as they grow older. I remember the delight with which a friend signed off her long career in public service when she was listed in the Queen's Birthday Honours as an M.B.E.

Rewards of those kinds are commensurate with effort put in over many years. They do not come easily, nor often to those who are young unless they make the headlines in sport or entertainment. They are not like the silver cups that were a reward for winning a school race, nor like the medals that were the fruit of heroic endeavour at war. No, these are rewards for experience and endurance. The retirement "honour", or retirement present, like the gold watch that marks long service, are not to be despised but should be given, received and cherished as a record of appreciation. Those who receive such honours and presents as the result of work or public service know very well that these rewards also honour those, such as members of their family, who made that reward possible. They also know that many more people deserve rewards than get them.

Public recognition of these kinds comes to relatively few people. On the other hand, most of us can look round our homes and see tokens of other people's affection for us, given to us simply because we have been loved as people by our spouses, partners, children and friends. As we grow older many of us know that perhaps we ought to throw out our youngest child's first rather lop-sided art-work attempt, or give a certain vase to the jumble sale, but we don't. Instead, we rearrange the clutter, sigh because of the extra dusting, and continue to treasure objects that have no value or meaning to other people but that are associated with powerful memories of events and people in our own lives.

These memories and our accumulated possessions are a reward in themselves. Sooner or later they may, however, become a problem: as we grow older we realize that we are going to have to leave some things behind us when we retire, grow too old to stay in our present home, or die. When I retire I shall not need all those books, journals and interesting bits of information that I have accumulated over the years. I shall need to burn them or leave them behind for others to use. I look forward to retirement day with pleasure, and am already anticipating it as I shed some of my out-of-date treasures which are of no use to anyone else, and bestow others on my children, younger colleagues and friends. At home there are many nice things I can give away to those who will enjoy them as much as I do. The older one gets, the closer to retirement, the surrender of one's independence, or death itself, the more pleasant it becomes to shed one's possessions in order to give pleasure to other people. When we begin to find that happening in our own lives we know that we have reached the time of anticipation.

Anticipations

Stronger by weakness, wiser men become,
As they draw near to their eternal home:
Leaving the old, both worlds at once view,
That stand upon the threshold of the new.[11]

One of the privileges of growing older is being able to look backwards and forwards at the same time. If it is to be a pleasure rather than a pain we must be able to anticipate old age and death with a realistic approach to finality. "No young man believes he shall ever die",[12] said William Hazlitt, but as we get older, and can no longer claim to be young, we know that we are going to die. Many of us do not find this a particularly pleasurable prospect, even though we often find ourselves apprehensive at the thought of living until we are very old. Whenever we prepare to leave one job for another, we are learning how to approach finality and death. Retirement itself is one of the most important opportunities we shall ever have of learning how to handle finality in a pleasurable way. All too often the other finalities in our lives, such as the breaking up of a marriage, or the death of relatives and friends, bring us excruciating pain rather than pleasure. When we retire, however, we have a chance to look at endings as beginnings.

I must admit that I look forward to retirement. It probably won't match my expectations. I know that I have not foreseen all the hazards I may have to face. Like many other people, I have found it hard to be realistic about the various possibilities that lie ahead. I tend to think that I shall be able to enjoy the relative freedom that not having paid employment will bring me. I imagine that I will adjust to a decreased income and that I shall continue to enjoy good health even if I suffer the inevitable diminishments of old age. I know that a fatal illness might strike me down at any time, but that is something I have always known. I think I am ready for anything – but I know that I am not. Despite this mixture of illusion and realism I believe that I shall be able to meet the future with a peaceful mind because I intend retirement to be a preparation for death, and I want to choose certain legacies to leave my children and friends. I have already spoken about giving away possessions, but the kind of legacy I am talking about is of a different nature.

Tucked away, up in the attic drawers, cardboard boxes and assorted packages, there is a kind of record of our personal family history. Some of it came to us through our own parents. I can still remember my grief when I uncovered one of my own letters to my mother, after she had died, but that sorrow was tinged with pleasure and pride that she had kept the letter of a six-year-old child for all that time as evidence of her love and care for me during my formative years. I'm glad she left something like that for me to find, and I intend to use the records we have accumulated to do something of the same kind for our children. My husband spent five years of his old age writing down his reminiscences of a long life, not for publication but for me and our children to be able to see his life as he saw it. He and I read what he wrote while he was still alive, so we enjoyed it together, and now our children have some good memories in those pages to cherish and hand on at a later date. When I retire I shall spend some time doing the same as he has done.

I know that I am not alone in these kinds of activities. I do not consider them to be morbid pursuits. I think it is sensible and proper to want to leave certain very personal records of our family history to our children, grandchildren and close friends. Some of us do that by leaving letters and written accounts, as my husband and I have done. Others do so through unexpected bequests that have meaning for themselves and their legatees. In my own life it has not been money that sweetened sorrow but the thoughtfulness of the benefactors, for in this way we have acquired precious mementoes of our relatives and friends.

People are often advised to make a will as soon as they have anything to leave to anybody, and to revise it at important stages in their lives, such as marriages or the arrival of grandchildren. Certainly it needs to be done long before one reaches senility. Most women and men accept the responsibility of making a will quite easily. They enjoy disposing of their property. They want to give pleasure to their children and close friends. They want to be remembered with affection and thankfulness. They often want to use legacies to support people or charities whose work they consider to be important. These people grow older knowing that they have the means to help a cause, work or charity to continue its task, and this gives them considerable pleasure.

Some people, however, find it impossible to make a will. Some cannot face the task: some believe they have nothing worthwhile to leave to anyone; others mean to do it but somehow never get round to translating their good intentions into reality. If they realized how much difficulty it will cause to those whom they love if they die intestate, I think they might be more willing to tackle the task, even though they do not find it in the least bit pleasurable.

People's attitudes towards wills and legacies are often indicative of their feelings about their own death. Anticipating death cannot be pleasurable for those who are young and healthy. As we grow older, however, we need to think about it constructively. Since we are individuals we will undertake this task at different times of our lives. My husband once told me that he did not think seriously about his own death until he was eighty years old. I began my own preparations for it in my sixtieth year of life. Much depends, I suppose, on how many years we think we have ahead of us. In former generations people's life expectancy was so short that the whole life was treated as a preparation for death, which was almost invariably seen as a gateway to a better existence. As late as the nineteenth century William Blake wrote a poem which refers to this sentiment and also points to the universality and inevitability of death:

> The door of death is made of gold,
> That mortal eyes cannot behold,
> But when the mortal eyes are closed,
> And cold and pale the limbs reposed,
> The soul awakes, and wandering, sees
> In her mild hand the golden keys.
> The grave is Heaven's golden gate,
> And rich and poor around it wait.[13]

At the time that Blake wrote that poem, belief in "life after death" was general. Among people living in countries which were formerly greatly influenced by Christianity that can no longer be said to be true. The rise of secular ideologies, such as materialism, together with the gradual decline of institutional Christianity, has weakened our faith and made many of us more unsure about what happens to us after we die, and this is especially true for Christians who have had to do their own thinking in a climate of theological controversy about the whole subject.

Many people are quite definite about their beliefs. Some hold that death is the end of existence of any kind. Others think of death as a kind of purifying process: for them reincarnation is a logical process and, according to the kind of life they have lived in one mode of existence, they expect to return to earthly existence in another form time and again until they are sufficiently holy not to have to return to earth but can be subsumed into "nirvana". Theories about reincarnation are not confined to Hindus and Buddhists but are more widespread, even being found among those who would feel themselves to be sincere Christians or agnostics. There is, however, no room for reincarnation in orthodox Christianity. According to its doctrines we have only one life here on earth, and what happens to us after death is determined by that single opportunity.

Christians are not asked to believe in personal immortality. They are asked to believe in resurrection and eternal life. Although the difference between these two doctrines is not always easy to understand, it is important to try to do so.[14] Those who believe in immortality see death as a release of the "soul" from its captivity in the body. Since for them the personality is an expression of the "soul", though not its totality, the essential "person" as known in life survives death and goes on. Christians who believe in eternal life agree that there is continuity between life and death, for we live in eternal life before, during and after death, but they also believe that their earthly bodies are "sown in corruption and raised in incorruption"[15], as St Paul said, and that their resurrection bodies will allow them to live in the presence of God in a new way. They are content to leave the mode of that existence to God. The distinction between immortality and eternal life may seem to be a fine one, but the difference may be brought out by saying that God alone is immortal: we being mortal serve God's immortality for eternity.

These issues about immortality and eternal life are complicated by various beliefs about purgatory, heaven and hell. Christians are divided about whether purgatory exists, what happens in it if it does, who qualifies for heaven and who for hell. Some still hold to beliefs about half-way houses, or "Limbo" for those who are not baptized Christians. It all sounds very complicated and it is. None of us will ever know the truth until we pass through that "golden gate" and then, if the "snuffed out for ever" theory is right, we shall never know anything any more. Those of us who believe in personal resurrection and in eternal life approach death with reverence as we try to live our lives now as a preparation for the next stage. We also accept that as we already live an eternal life we can catch glimpses of the resurrection life to come, here and now. I see that "life beyond" more and more as I grow older. It is these glimpses, "seen through a glass darkly", that helps me to see death in the context of God's immortality, a context I first saw when I was a young woman and read Tolstoy's *War and Peace*, where he says:

Man is a being beyond time and beyond space who is conscious of himself in the conditions of space and time. One should conquer the fear of death, and when you cease to fear it, you cease to serve yourself as mortal, and you will serve an immortal God from whom you came and to whom you are going.[16]

God is immortal. We live in his eternity. Our mortality is safe in God's providence. These are the messages which have given me confidence to go on towards death. Although I have certainly not yet conquered my fear of death, I know that I want to serve God, from whom I came and to whom I am going.

Preparing for death is an important part of that journey. So it is a pleasure as well as a problem. The pleasure is in the fact of death: the problems come with the contemplation of the process of dying, which began as soon as I was born and will be completed when I go through the gate of death. I shall be writing about some of the problems of dying later on (see pages 123–8 and 165–9). Here, when I refer to the fact of death as welcome, I do not mean that I regard death as a release from the problems of a painful and debilitating illness or extreme old age, for I see death as far more than a release. Teilhard de Chardin once said: "We must overcome death by finding God in it."[17] As I grow older I know that I will meet death among my friends more often than I did when I was younger. I know that I will come to it myself. As a Christian I try to greet death as a friend, knowing that I want to find God in it. And when I lose my way, become afraid, feel repulsed at the thought of dying, as I often do, I turn to George Fox who wrote:

> I saw that there was an ocean of darkness and death, but that an infinite ocean of light and love flowed over the ocean of darkness. In that I saw the infinite love of God.[18]

Then from these words I go to the Bible, and to any of a number of well loved sayings which sustain my Christian hope, deepen my faith and inspire me to respond to that "infinite love of God" with love and confidence.[19]

Standing where I do, at the point in my life which I have now reached, where I can view both worlds at once, I thank God for the gift of life and trust that I shall be able to use my remaining years wisely and "with understanding".[20] If I am to do that, if any of us are to do that, we must face the problems of growing older with realism and a determination to overcome our diminishments and difficulties as far as it is possible to do so. This is a very practical task for which we will need to be equipped with a good deal of common sense and courage.

2

The Problems of Growing Older

Introduction / Diminishments in general / Physical diminishments: loss of sensory functions; motor power; sexual strength; sleep ability; memory and intellect / Psychological diminishments; loss of mental agility; adaptability; ability to suppress unpleasant character traits / Social diminishments: marginalization; loss of independence; bereavements; loss of wealth and status / Spiritual diminishments: general; lost opportunities for reconciliation; effects of past failures; self-pity; loss of belief in the face of death; death itself.

All would live long but none would be old.[1]

Introduction

I am not sure how old Benjamin Franklin was when he wrote those lines. His life lasted a long time, for he was eighty-four years old when he died. Certainly the dread of old age afflicts most of us when we are young enough to view it objectively and, as Franklin says, it is not the fear of longevity itself that is off-putting: rather we fear the possible consequences of becoming very old.

I have a vivid memory of the fear and disgust that overwhelmed me when, as a medical student, I visited a psycho-geriatric ward full of senile old ladies. I was inexperienced and gauche. I did not begin to know how to talk to anyone. The patient who had been assigned to my care for the day called for her mother in a high-pitched whining voice at ten second intervals for the whole morning. It was a tremendous relief when she temporarily stopped whining while she gobbled up her lunch and then slumped into her chair for her afternoon sleep. When she woke up she was wet, smelly and irritable. The whining started up again, interspersed this time with a rich variety of swear words that embarrassed me.

As we made our way to the bathroom to change her clothes, one of the older nurses said to her: "You are a naughty girl today, Rosa, playing up the young doctor like that." Rosa stopped, swung herself round to face me, bared her gums in a ferocious grin and said in a clear voice: "She doesn't like me and I don't like her; so there!"

It was true. I felt ashamed. At that moment I wanted to run away, out of the ward, out of medical school, out of my chosen profession so that I could avoid the truth that I was going to meet many Rosas in my life and didn't know how I was ever going to learn to like them. My guilt was all mixed up with indignation that the nurse should have addressed an octogenarian as if she were a little girl. I was, of course, projecting my own attitudes on to the nurse. My anger should have been directed towards myself for my own patronizing attitudes towards elderly people. I did not run away, but by the end of the day I left the ward with relief, thankful only that I did not have to go back there the next day. I was shaken and only partially comforted by my tutor's perceptive understanding of my conflicting reactions to the encounter.

I never met Rosa again, and it was more than twenty years before I ventured back into a locked ward in a psychiatric hospital. When I did go back it was to another hospital, and I went there as a woman of forty-six, with a great deal of experience as a family doctor behind me. This time I was a mature student of psychiatry, able to see things rather differently, and to learn what I needed to learn about senile dementia. My daily contact with patients over a period of a year's training helped to evict many of my residual fears. I began to see old people like Rosa as individuals despite their profound imprisonment in the shackles of dementia. That perception of them as persons does not lessen the difficulty of looking after someone who has ceased to function effectively, nor does it abolish the inherent and natural fear of becoming senile oneself. It does, however, help people like me to treat individuals with the respect they deserve, and to begin to love them and even to like them. My contact with that ward bore good fruit, and when I returned to general practice I carried with me a better understanding of some of the problems of old age.

I now see dementia differently from the way I saw it as a young medical student. I see it as a disease which needs to be conquered as far as it may be for some people, as nature's compassionate friend for others, and as a vocation for a few of God's chosen servants. I shall say more about that later on (see pages 84–90). Here, I refer to this personal experience to show that it is possible for one's attitudes towards the problems of old age to change and develop. Growing older in itself can help many of us to move towards our own old age with an equanimity and fortitude we could not have possessed when we were young adults.

I know that Rosa, and the others like her whom I met during my course in adult psychiatry, have improved my own attitude towards ageing in general. Yet, as I grow older I still find some of the diminishments of life quite difficult to bear.

Diminishments in General

Many people as they grow older fear the coming of old age. They regret the failing of physical and mental powers, the withdrawal from active life, posts of leadership and the satisfaction of being used creatively. These increasing diminishments can be seen as a hollowing out of the material and the temporal, in order to be ready to be filled with the spiritual and the eternal.[2]

The first time I heard the word "diminishments" used by anyone it was from the lips of a close friend who had recently retired. She had come to stay with us during her convalescence from an operation for breast cancer. Her wound was not yet fully healed so I dressed it. The ugly scar ran across her flattened chest wall, the absence of one breast made more apparent by the remaining one. She was embarrassed. "My first diminishment", she said. "Yes", I replied, ignorant of the nuance and importance to her of that word, for she was an ardent follower of Teilhard de Chardin and was referring to a passage in one of his books that I knew nothing about at the time she spoke.

The moment passed. Within two years my friend was dead. Just before she went into hospital for the last time she gave me some of her books. It was then that I came across the quotation she evidently had had in her mind when she spoke of her first diminishment:

When the signs of age begin to mark my body (and still more when they touch my mind); when the ill that is to diminish me or carry me off strikes from without or is born within me; when the painful moment comes in which I suddenly awaken to the fact that I am ill or growing old; and above all at that last moment when I feel I am losing hold of myself and am absolutely passive within the hands of the great unknown forces that have formed me; in all these dark

moments, O God, grant that I may understand
that it is You (provided only my faith is strong
enough) who are painfully parting the fibres of
my being in order to penetrate to the very
marrow of my substance and bear me away
within yourself.[3]

My friend died a painful and ugly death: by the time
I last saw her alive she was a victim of brain
secondaries, obsessed by a belief that all who were
caring for her were deliberately poisoning her. She
had lost all her hair because of the treatement she
had been given in a vain effort to save her life. Her
body had shrunk to a pitiful travesty of her former
self. She had lost all semblance of the religious faith
that had been so strong in her adult life.

I, and the other friends who lived through those
last few months with her, found the manner of her
dying almost unbearable, not least because of her loss
of faith. She had not been granted Teilhard de
Chardin's knowledge that God was "painfully parting the fibres" of her being, nor had she felt with
George Appleton that she was being made "ready to
be filled with the spiritual and the eternal". Those
words were there for me to cling to, but her anchors
had disappeared altogether, swept away in the storm
of her illness and annihilated by an invasive cancer in
her brain. Paradoxically, and for no obvious reason,
my faith deepened as hers weakened. Perhaps she
gave me the present of her faith? I am not sure. I can
only say what happened to me. Others have described
similar experiences.

My own first "dark moment" came within a few months of my friend's death, when my dentist told me I must lose one of my front teeth. I realized that the loss was not only permanent but an intimation of ageing that I could not resist. It was absurd to worry about the loss of one tooth and to rebel against the false one I acquired, but I did. Like everyone else who knows what it is to grow older, I came to terms with my condition and adapted to it without too much difficulty. Since then I have lived through many other small diminishments. I am aware of my own mortality. I am as prepared as I can be for every diminishment ahead, even the one I still fear the most, that of the possibility that I too will become, like Rosa, senile and helpless, "sans teeth, sans eyes, sans everything". What will be, will be. Moreover it will happen in different ways to everyone. Some diminishment of our powers seems to be an inevitable part of growing older, and we need to look carefully and realistically at some of these in order to be able to overcome them when we can and accept them when we can't.

Physical Diminishments

Ageing affects everyone differently. The rate at which various physical diminishments and ailments affect people varies from one person to the next. If you and I live long enough a time will come when sight, hearing, taste and smell will lose some of their sharpness. We will become less mobile than we are now. Our reflexes will work more slowly. If we live long enough to grow old, the natural ageing of our bodies will eventually take its toll of our strength, even though we may be spared from serious illness. Some common hazards of being old are well known to everyone.

Loss of sensory functions

Some of the physical diminishments that come to most people are so obvious that they cannot be ignored easily. When the words on a printed page become blurred, for instance, we know it is time to visit the optician.

VISUAL IMPAIRMENT

The gradual loss of sight is one of the most difficult diminishments that human beings have to bear. Many people have to wear spectacles, although there are some whose eyesight remains keen even when they are very old indeed. Wearing glasses is no hardship at all compared with the plight of some old people who also have to struggle with low visual aids such as hand-held magnifying glasses. You only have to watch someone trying to balance a book on one hand while using the other to steady a magnifying glass, when his or her muscles are weak and shaky, to realize just how difficult it is to get any pleasure out of reading in those kinds of circumstance. If the person's intellect is undiminished the frustration may be intense. Someone who suffers from this degree of sight impairment will be unlikely to be able to use teletext or find the numbers on a conventional telephone at all easily. They cannot drive a car, and even the pleasure of being driven is partly lost when one cannot see properly. I have, perhaps, described the worst that can happen to a very old person. Blindness itself is a tragedy, but there is more help available for people who are registered as blind than there is for those whose acuity is severely impaired but who are not yet registered as partly-sighted. There are far more old people about with severe impairment of vision than with partial sight, and these are the ones who need more attention than they are presently getting. Those of us who care for elderly people cannot be surprised that so many of them are reduced to sitting in an upright fireside chair, when we realize what a struggle it is to retain interest in former pleasures or to develop new skills to replace the ones that have been lost.

HEARING DIFFICULTIES

Hearing impairments are rather like visual ones in that they tend to make themselves obvious to us. When it becomes difficult to hear something someone else is saying to us in a crowded room, we know that our hearing is becoming impaired even though we may not yet need a hearing aid.

Hearing impairment is an isolating handicap. It is one which interferes with many people's enjoyment of life, often when they are still comparatively young.

Going to parties ceases to be pleasurable when it is difficult to hear what is being said. Wearing a hearing aid in such circumstances can be unpleasant, for everything is magnified and the resultant cacophony, mixed up with the occasional whistle from a malfunctioning aid, is a positive deterrent to socialization. At home everyone else has to suffer if the hearing impaired member of the family is to enjoy listening to the radio, record player or television.

It may seem relatively easy to overcome some of the difficulties, but before people can make good use of such ways of countering their handicap they have to acknowledge their problem. It is well known that it is very difficult to acknowledge one's own hearing impairment, or to know exactly when to start making moves towards a suitable hearing aid. Moreover, hearing aids sometimes cause more frustration than relief, and fiddling about to get them to work is not always easy for older people with stiff fingers. It should not surprise anyone, though it does, to find that so many old people have put their hearing aid away in their drawers. They prefer to sit in their chairs, "dreaming dreams",[4] listening to internal memories and hopes for the future rather than trying to take in what is going on outside their narrowed orbit of hearing. They often repel visitors in subtle ways and seem to prefer their own company, and this can cause intense distress to families and friends. It is a condition that calls for a great deal of understanding and sensitivity on all sides if older hearing impaired people are to be helped to stay in touch (see also page 157).

LOSS OF SMELL AND TASTE

Unlike visual and hearing impairments, some sensory losses are harder to appreciate because they are more gradual. The senses of smell and taste, for instance, gradually diminish over a period of years. Other people may notice that we have lost them earlier than we do ourselves.

I first noticed this when I asked myself why so many of the older patients I knew when I was a family doctor smelt slightly stale? The answer came in two parts. One reason was that people get used to their own smells: the other that people's ability to smell and taste grow less as they grow older. Many old people don't notice their body smell or even the smell of their incontinence. You and I need to be alert to these facts, so that we can prevent ourselves from being the cause of other people's distress. We will not be able to rely on our own senses of smell and taste as the sole guide to our cleanliness, but will need, for instance, to be scrupulous about our personal hygiene. We may have to force ourselves to take extra baths and change our clothing more frequently as we grow older. Therein lies another problem.

As people grow older their energy diminishes. It becomes more difficult to step in and out of a bath. It takes extra effort to bend down to a bottom drawer to get out clean underclothes. It is not easy to take clothes to be laundered or dry-cleaned at regular intervals. It becomes harder to change bed linen regularly. Sometimes outside observers, accustomed to the fastidiousness of their parents, relatives, friends or clients in their younger years, are surprised and even disgusted by the changes that overtake these same people when they reach old age. People who are middle-aged, when their senses are relatively intact, will need to develop good strategies to help them when they reach old age. Finding an understanding daughter, son or younger friend who is prepared to be honest about smells and stains on clothes is one such strategy. Developing routine habits of bathing and changing that are strong enough to hold through thick and thin is another. Learning to accept help graciously will also stand anyone in good stead when they become old enough to need assistance in washing and dressing.

Smell plays an important part in people's ability to enjoy their food, for a good smell enhances the ability of the tongue's taste buds to discriminate between different kinds of food. Older people often lose their ability to enjoy food because they cannot smell its delicious aromas or taste its seasoning as well as they could when they were younger. Some old people will complain of severe loss of appetite because of this, stop eating good food and become quite ill through undernourishment. Relatives who care for such people have a hard time finding means of preparing and seasoning food in ways that will stimulate the appetite, but it can be done if the carers ignore the messages of their own smell and taste organs.

So far I have concentrated on some of the better known sensory impairments which affect older people's lives. In many ways, however, some other diminishments are even more important because they are the more dangerous for being less noticeable.

LOSS OF TOUCH, POSITION AND BALANCE SENSES

As people grow older they gradually lose their sense of touch, position and balance. Reflexes slow down. Muscles and joints respond less readily to command. Hand-eye co-ordination becomes more difficult.

The results of such slow bodily changes are sometimes more obvious to others than to those afflicted by them. Many older people, for instance, do not notice that they are no longer able to co-ordinate movements quickly, or judge distance properly. They no longer drive a car as well as they used to. Passengers are all too well aware of that fact, and may find themselves increasingly reluctant to accept an invitation "to go for a drive". If the passengers try to persuade the old person to give up driving they are likely to provoke an indignant reaction, both because the driver has not noticed his or her bad driving and also because older people are often very reluctant to relinquish their freedom to go where they like, when they like. Moreover, the medical examinations that most insurance companies insist on for drivers who are over seventy years old cannot always simulate driving conditions closely enough to be able to pick out those whose reflexes are too slow to respond quickly to emergencies. In consequence many older people continue to drive when they are no longer safe on the roads.

Although old people may retain the physical ability to climb ladders or stand on chairs to reach something they want from the top of a cupboard, the impairment of their ability to balance themselves properly may cause them to fall. Accidents like these happen not only because of loss of balance but also because of a diminution in touch. Older people's feet simply don't have the feeling in them that they used to. They stumble more easily, especially when negotiating steps, turning quickly, stepping over kerb stones or carpet edges. Impaired sensation, poor balance and slowed reflexes can then combine to cause disaster. Many older people become really old when they break a leg or arm bone in one of these ways.

All of us will experience some loss of balance and touch as we grow older. The consequent difficulties may be compounded by a reduction in motor power, which happens when our bones become brittle and we lose some muscular power and joint flexibility.

Loss of motor power

Provided that people's brains and nerves are healthy, most men and women will find that they can move many of their muscles at will and go where they want to go. The muscles involved in locomotion are often called "voluntary muscles" because they move on command. Those involved in other bodily functions, such as muscles concerned with breathing and digestion, are sometimes called "involuntary muscles", and I have used this distinction in considering what loss of motor power involves.

DIMINISHING VOLUNTARY MOTOR POWER

Muscles waste as people grow older. Bones lose some of their calcium, and become less dense and more friable; those who happen to fall are more likely than younger people to break a bone, often one of the leg bones. Knowing this, many people need to be more observant about various hazards in the home that might cause them to trip or fall off ladders and furniture when, for instance, they are trying to change window curtains. Ageing itself, however, often seems to affect people's ability to see themselves as they are. All too often they, and we, will deny any loss of mobility, ignore the obvious signs of danger and pretend to be young enough to do without a stick or ask for that vital help in changing curtains or trying to wash the windows.

It is comparatively easy to delude ourselves. We can always point to someone else who is older than we are and who can still do what we think we ought to be able to do, but often can't. Most of us can come to terms with what we can and cannot do without casting too many sideways glances at other people's skills and abilities. It is, I think, important to be able to acknowledge our limitations before, and not after our first major accident or illness acquired through overstretching ourselves. Yet how difficult it is to do that without becoming afraid and unable to do anything in the least bit adventurous. Finding the right balance between a proper fear and a proper determination to overcome handicap is one of the challenges that come to us as we are growing older.

Hazards come to us because of our brittle bones. We also get into trouble because of ageing joints. Joints lose some of their elasticity and the joint linings become roughened. People tend to find that they are not as strong as they were when they were younger. Their joints creak and are stiff in the early mornings, even if they are spared from arthritis. Very old people become more bowed and begin to shuffle, or, at the least, to walk with a rounded swing of the legs at joints, which makes their gait somewhat ungainly.

This loss of power is largely due to the natural ageing of bones, muscles and joints. Provided that these muscles have a healthy nerve supply they will go on doing what they are told to do, though not as well as when their owners were young. Other muscles in the body, however, are not under people's direct control. These involuntary smooth muscles in gut, bladder and uterus, for instance, or specialized muscles that work the heart and bronchial tubes, also waste as people grow older.

LOSS OF INVOLUNTARY MUSCLE POWER

Involuntary muscle wasting means that as people grow older their natural functions inevitably slow down. Constipation is common. Men find it difficult to relax their sphincters and contract their bladders in order to micturate. (Prostatic problems are different and will be dealt with later – see pages 153–5). Women's lives are often seriously affected by urgency and/or stress incontinence.

Older people have good reason to fret about their bowel and bladder functions. It is no easy task to keep oneself "on the move" at a time in one's life when it is becoming difficult to chew bulky high fibre foods like cabbage, apples and bran biscuits, and positively unpleasant to court "wind" by eating too many baked beans, even though they are rich in fibre. It is small wonder that many old people turn to beer, prunes, porridge and, sometimes, more dangerous laxatives, to help them avoid the distressing symptoms of chronic constipation. It is not surprising either to find that many older people are not keen on travel when it means worrying about the possibility of their being overtaken by a sudden desire to pass water when there are no toilet facilities easily available. Urinary incontinence is very embarrassing in such circumstances.

Older people are often sensitive about their natural functions. Those of us who are younger, or have not yet encountered any of these problems, need to try to understand and sympathize with men and women who seem to worry excessively about their bowels and bladders.

Loss of muscular power of all kinds is difficult to bear. It is frustrating to have an active mind when one's body won't respond to its initiatives and good intentions. By the time we are eighty we nearly all feel our age and, as the psalmist observed, "though men be so strong that they come to fourscore years: yet is their strength then but labour and sorrow; so soon passeth it away, and we are gone".[5]

As we get older many of us will know that we are losing our strength in a variety of ways. We sometimes say that we feel "weak all over", or that we are "wearing out". This sense of attrition is increased when we notice a diminution of sexual strength.

Loss of sexual strength

There is a wide variation in individual need for sexual intercourse, and there are no "norms" about frequency of sexual activity. If these facts were widely understood and accepted many people would be far happier about their sexual lives than they are, but we live at a time when people's sexual activities are openly discussed, and this can have unfortunate effects on some people. A well publicized fact about one eighty-year-old man's procreative ability, for instance, can be reassuring to some men of comparable age who are still sexually active, but will be seen as a reproach by other eighty-year-olds who are impotent or only mildly interested in sexual activity of any kind. By contrast, if someone refers to one seventy-five-year old man as "a dirty old man" in the presence of another of the same age who is still sexually active, the second man may feel himself to be abnormal when he is not. Similar feelings may be engendered in women when other people say things like "she ought to know better at her time of life". The truth is that people are individuals with individual "norms".

Men and women should respect their own patterns of sexual behaviour rather than comparing themselves with other people. They should also pay attention to how they feel about their needs, or lack of needs. A man of seventy-five and a woman of sixty, for instance, may still enjoy sexual intercourse. If he develops heart disease and gets severe angina whenever he tries to make love to his partner, both of them are likely to find reasons for avoiding full sexual intercourse. In such circumstances it is perfectly possible for them to give each other intense sexual pleasure and to reach orgasm by fondling and kissing each other.

In different circumstances a widower of seventy might be upset because he still needs sexual intercourse. He may feel disloyal to his former wife if he starts looking for another sexual partner too soon. Such a man may need to be reassured about his sexual desires, and helped to realize that his wife's death has released him from his marriage vows so that he is free to seek another partner whenever he is ready to do so, irrespective of other people's opinions about the propriety of his actions. Another person of the same age and sex may feel that he neither needs sexual intercourse nor wants to seek another partner. He is content with masturbation, or, perhaps, finds that the desire for orgasm has faded altogether. This man needs to feel as at ease with his decisions as the man who seeks another sexual partner.

What I have said about men also applies to women. Moreover, there are many older people who want to marry, or live together, for companionship rather than sexual intercourse with each other. There is nothing wrong in that either so long as they talk to each other beforehand about their expectations.

It is, I think, sensible to recognize and accept one's own feelings and patterns of behaviour as normative for oneself. It is also important to know that these feelings do not remain constant throughout one's life. Circumstances change and we change with them.

It goes without saying, yet needs to be repeated, that it is not sexual intercourse but love for each other which binds people together. Love outlasts sexual desire. No partnership need necessarily break up just because two people have lost their sexual impetus. Neither partner need feel inadequate because their needs have changed. Some partnerships can, and do, survive even though one or both people have to come to terms with unpleasant discoveries about themselves as they grow older together.

Although I have placed sensory impairments, loss of motor power and sexual strength within the broad category of physical diminishments I am aware that the psychological effects of physical decline are often more serious than the physical insult of not being able to see, hear, move about or have sexual intercourse as often as one did when young. Nothing that happens to people's bodies leaves their minds and spirits untouched. Similarly, what happens to them mentally and emotionally can affect their bodies.

There is always an interplay between body, mind and spirit, and this is especially true of certain physiological functions such as sleep, where the physical consequences of growing older sometimes have psychological and spiritual consequences which cause problems.

Sleep-related difficulties

As people grow older they tend to need less continuous sleep and more naps. That fairly sweeping generalization is based on scientific observation, but it does not particularly help an older individual who stays awake half the night and then finds himself or herself falling asleep at awkward moments during the day. Some people can meet their diminishing need for continuous sleep, and their increasing need for short spells of sleep during the day, with equanimity, especially after retirement: it is less easy to make provision for a nap after lunch when one is at work. Many others, however, are very upset by insomnia and daytime napping: they cannot understand that older brains function better on the whole with this kind of sleep pattern than with that more commonly found in younger people. Insomnia is often a problem to older people because of the brooding anxieties and unpleasant thoughts that come to them during the night and early hours of the morning. These are the people who sometimes fall victim to habit-forming drugs taken to induce sleep, or to keep them asleep, because they cannot tolerate being awake when other members of the household are happily sleeping the night away.

Sleeping pills have adverse effects on the natural rhythms of the brain during ordinary sleep. They also cause some degree of slowed reflexes and confusion in the brain. Many old people who take sleeping drugs suffer from side effects when they try to get up during the night, or in the early morning: at such times they may stumble and fall and hurt themselves quite badly; alternatively, they may make errors of judgement, such as taking another sleeping pill when it's time to get up, or forget their daytime medication altogether, thus harming their health. Moreover, these drugs slow the mind for longer than people think. They have a marked tendency to cause mid-morning confusion, irritability and agitated depression. Many older people do not recognize the connection between their condition and the pills they took the night before: they frequently insist on having their night pill, even if it is habit-forming and hazardous to their health. Unfortunately some sleeping pills can damage old people's livers and kidneys as well as increasing their mental confusion.

Those of us who are growing older need to be very circumspect in our demands for continuous sleep. It is better to make provision for the daytime naps we know we shall need than to insist on going to sleep at 10 or midnight every night, and staying asleep until 7.00 or 8.00 every morning, but then feeling wretched until lunchtime.

I am well aware of how awful insomnia can be and I also know that there are times, after a severe operation or bereavement, for instance, when sleep-inducing drugs can offer merciful relief to a person and should not be withheld. There are, however, better ways of helping ourselves to deal with natural changes in our sleep patterns as we grow older. These include making sure that we are warm, comfortable and not hungry when we go to bed; that we learn how to relax and drift into sleep; that we have a pleasing distraction to turn to when we cannot sleep because the anxieties of the day are catching up with us. Some of us can benefit from relaxation therapy, self-hypnosis, or "sleep tapes" which offer a kind of instant hypnotherapy that can be very helpful. Such simple methods can be effective and they do not damage the brain.

Daytime napping is often embarrassing to middle-aged people but less so to elderly folk, who have learnt the art of musing gently to themselves. I often wonder whether those of us who are young and middle aged should be as upset as we often are by the sight of very elderly people "doing nothing". Sitting in a chair, cat-napping and dreaming about the past may be nature's way of helping old people to let go of some pleasures in order to focus on eternity. The relative isolation of "being" rather than "doing and communicating" may be God's way of helping some people to step out of one kind of life into another mode of existence beyond death.

As we find some purpose to those physical diminishments that we have seen relatives and friends enduring, and which we are likely to face ourselves in the future, we can, I think, understand Sybil Harton's desire for self-surrender, as expressed in this passage from her monograph *On Growing Old*:

> We go forward with both hands outstretched to take whatever conditions God decrees, and to like them, positively like them, because they are his will.[6]

We might like to go forward into the future with "both hands outstretched" but many of us do not find it at all easy to face the diminishments that come to us as we grow older, nor do we like them very much. Still less do we like the mental changes that come upon us as we age.

Loss of memory and intellect

When I was a young woman I was an avid reader. Unlike today's medical students, who rarely have time to read anything except their textbooks, we were encouraged to widen our horizons, and I spent some time during my university years attending lectures on poetry and literature. I can remember to this day coming upon Helen Waddell's classic love story about Peter Abelard and Heloise,[7] because I read it when I was in love myself, knowing that I was about to lose my beloved man to another woman. The author's perception of the ecstasy and pathos of passion stirred me to the depths of my being. Later I read just about everything she had written, and, as the young do, allowed my enthusiasms to bubble over into almost every conversation. One day, after a lecture on philosophy, during which Helen Waddell's work on the medieval scholastics[8] had been mentioned, I shared my enthusiasm with an older friend who knew her.

"It's very sad, isn't it?" he said. "She's dementing, you know."

I did not know. It was a profound shock. "That beautiful, clear, logical blend of reason and passion," I thought, "all swept away." My mind recalled my whining Rosa, crying pitifully for her mother. I shuddered, shrugged my shoulders, as if to ward off the spectre of myself in old age, and turned aside to get on with more pleasant things to say and do: but I did not forget.

As a working family doctor I have met many Rosas and Helens in various stages of this most cruel diminishment that life can offer. As they grow older people lose the clarity and sharp recall of memory that they had when they were young. They find it difficult to remember someone's name although the person they are greeting is well known to them. Their memory plays tricks on them: they can, for instance, suddenly recall events that happened long ago, whereas they cannot remember what they had to eat at their last meal. Those kinds of experience are universal. We, too, are likely to suffer them. In some people, fewer I think than many of us realize, memory impairment will be followed by intellectual deterioration: when it does the victims' ability to think rationally deteriorates; they can no longer find their way home if they go out; they forget how to cook a meal, clean house and generally care for themselves. In short, they become senile.

Senile dementia does not seem so bad if it overtakes very old and infirm people. The fear that many of us carry around is of its happening when we are still quite young and comparatively vigorous in physical health. Voicing my own fear about this to a nurse colleague on one occasion, I found myself greatly helped by her cheerful comment:

"Why worry?" she said. "If it happens to us we shan't know. It'll upset others, yes, but not us. Anyway, you can't do anything about it, you know."

Her remark was only partly true. Some people do sense that they are going senile in the early stages of the process, and some can be helped by certain medical procedures. My friend's reference to the quirkiness of "fate", however, reflected a reality I needed to hear at that moment. We laughed and got on with the job we were doing together.

My memories of many senile people have been sweetened by what they taught me. I have already mentioned Rosa's perceptive remark, which helped me to look at my own attitudes towards elderly and disabled people. The incident with her is matched by another with a patient in the community for whom I had cared for many years. Towards the end of her life she had become bedridden and quite locked away inside her own thoughts. On calling in one day I found her in bed, her three cats curled up beside her. She was lying somewhat askew and looked very uncomfortable. Her daughter and I moved her to a more comfortable position. Suddenly she opened her eyes, looked straight at me and said: "Thank you for your care for me." They were words which dated back to the time many years before when I had cradled her in my arms after the sudden and tragic death of her husband. Those were the very words she had said to me after the funeral. Now, she and I were united in a memory of a harsh time in her life, one that was followed by a long and courageous struggle against her own painful disablement from a severe form of chronic arthritis.

This patient's thanks fed my spirit and helped me to understand that I simply did not know what was going on inside her locked up mind, or in those of many other equally infirm patients and friends. Quite recently I came upon another passage in Sybil Harton's book, *On Growing Old*, which expresses this in a helpful way:

> All nature grows in the dark and it is God's providence which ordains who it is who needs that darkness of mind and sense in which the spirit can fulfil its final consummation. We do not know at what perfection they are inwardly gazing, who endure this strange state of senile decay.[9]

Before I end this section on the diminishments of mental powers that lead to "this strange state" I must return to Helen Waddell because she represents a number of people who, I believe, are called by God to this peculiar form of suffering. Her biographer, Dame Felicitas Corrigan, has written of a day in 1952 when a friend, Nicole Vraudemer (Mme de Praigny) went to visit her. By this time Helen was well into her dementia. Later her friend described her on that day:

> I see her now as she sat with her hands folded on her knees in her sitting-room in front of a small picture of Christ stumbling under the burden of his Cross.
>
> With tears in her eyes she said: "My cross is very heavy too and is crushing me but, looking at him I try to carry it without being too complaining or sorry for myself."[10]

Helen was sixty-three years old at the time of her friend's visit. She carried her cross for thirteen more years before she died.

I cannot offer a rational explanation of Helen Waddell's attitude towards her suffering, nor of her "calling" to it: nor do I pretend to understand the mystery of suffering. I do, however, believe that intercessory prayer and suffering are closely linked in some people's lives. When they pray for others they seem to be led by God to make an offering of themselves as a gift which can be used by God in whatever way God chooses. Their prayers become a kind of loving energy to be given away to others: yet at the same time the one who prays in this way is being replenished and nourished by the Holy Spirit, whose supply of love is inexhaustible. In some mysterious way these people are taken up into Christ's suffering. They are called to suffer in their flesh as they "complete what is lacking in Christ's affliction for the sake of his body, that is the Church',[11] and discover for themselves the truth of St Paul's great affirmation:

> I have been crucified with Christ; it is no longer I who live, but Christ who lives in me; and the life I now live in the flesh I live by faith in the Son of God, who loved me and gave himself for me.[12]

As a Christian I believe that some of God's servants experience that link between intercession and suffering in a continuous way. Others of us are spared that task but nevertheless know we sometimes share in Christ's work in less onerous but still costly ways. If that is so then we will know from experience the truth of another of St Paul's sayings:

> For as we share abundantly in Christ's suffering, so through Christ we share abundantly in comfort too.[13]

Like everyone else I shrink from suffering, and would certainly never court it, nor refuse its alleviation if that were possible. Nevertheless, as a Christian I can see some purpose in it, even though I do not understand why God permits it. If, in God's providence, Helen's kind of suffering comes to me, so be it. I just hope that my relatives and friends will love me enough to cherish my body and help me to endure it. At the same time, I pray to be spared from it.

Even if we are spared some of the worst ravages of physical diminishment most of us are likely to have to endure some psychological diminishments as we grow older.

Psychological Diminishments

Helen Waddell's loss of memory and intellectual powers were due to the destruction of her brain cells on a massive scale. All of us will suffer some loss of brain cells as they and we grow older, but we will be spared from dementia. Instead we may suffer some loss of mental agility. This condition has a physical component to it but the psychological effects predominate.

Loss of mental agility

As we grow older most of us will become a little forgetful, a little less able to grasp new ideas quickly, a little more muddled in our thinking. All of us, in some way or another, have to face some diminution in our ability to learn new skills or to acquire new knowledge for the first time. Those who are young can change from one job or profession quite easily. Those of us who are growing older do not find that so easy to do, especially if the new skills we are trying to acquire need us to have quick reaction and a retentive memory.

Within living memory human beings who live in industrialized nations have benefited from technology. Advances in electronic engineering, and the use of the silicon chip, for instance, have changed people's working lives. Everyone has had to adapt to the advent of calculators and computers. That kind of adjustment is relatively easy to make, but at the sharp end of the technological revolution there are hundreds and thousands of employees who find their work changed overnight in ways that tax their mental abilities. Some find they cannot adapt and have to retire early. Others struggle with it and manage to learn the new skills. The cost of that success may be high, for the anxiety and strain involved take a physical and psychological toll that can be quite unpleasant.

There is a price to be paid for every industrial advance, and it is paid by individuals in society. Stress contributes to the premature death of many comparatively young men and women from heart disease, strokes, lung cancer and suicidal depression, to name some of the more important of the diseases where stress is one of the causative factors. Western society, as a whole, does not take sufficient account of the strain it imposes on its middle-aged citizens when it asks them to make rapid changes in their working practices and acquire new skills almost overnight. Many personal tragedies can be avoided if those in charge of industry can be persuaded to care about the way in which they introduce cost effective changes to their employees.

The stresses and strains of modern life do not necessarily impair people's physical health: nevertheless, as they grow older many human beings experience certain losses and bereavements that affect their psychological health in quite concrete ways.

Loss of adaptability

Many people find that one of the consequences of growing older is that they become less adaptable and flexible than they were when they were younger. They like to know where they are. They need to leave space and time for themselves to achieve what they want to do without becoming flustered. If they cannot do that they find themselves in trouble.

I remember one friend, whom I'll call Jean, though that is not her real name, nor would you recognize her if you met her in the street. I watched Jean growing older for some twenty years. When she was a young middle-aged woman she crammed each day full with all kind of activities. She was a busy, competent, caring professional colleague. She would always find time to take on an extra activity, an extra responsibility, or to slip in an extra visit to a client. Those of us who worked with her knew that if we wanted a task well done we could turn to her. We failed to notice that she was growing older. Then one day I asked her to make an extra visit to a difficult demanding old lady.

"No, Una," Jean said, "I'm going to have lunch today."

I looked at her in amazement. In those days all of us took it for granted that we ate a sandwich and grabbed a cup of coffee at some time in the day when we could stop for five minutes. That way we could look forward to a comparatively early home-going and a leisured evening meal. Her remark was so unlike her.

"OK. I'll do it myself, then," I said, trying to conceal my astonishment. I looked at Jean. Her cheeks reddened. She burst into tears.

"I can't do it any more," she said. "I simply can't."

I don't think I really understood then, but a few months ago I found myself in a similar situation and realized that I was growing older myself and would have to change my own life style to take account of my diminishing ability to make rapid adjustments to each day's demands. I needed more time and space to accomplish my tasks. By that time Jean had been dead for some years, but the memory of her on that day so long ago came back to me, and so did that of the way she successfully managed the changes she had to make in order to stay the kind, patient and helpful colleague she had remained until her retirement. I too hope to grow old gracefully, as she did.

Loss of ability to suppress unpleasant character traits

Diminishments such as loss of adaptability and lack of energy, together with a certain sadness that one can no longer do things as quickly or as well as before, do impose their own strain on the psyche. If sixty-five-year-old men and women are foolish enough to go on trying to live as if they were twenty-five years old they may be proud of their pretence but they will pay the price for it psychologically, in that they will find their ability to suppress disagreeable character traits will be diminished. Tendencies to irritability, impatience and downright unpleasantness will increase.

Many people become more garrulous as they grow older, more inconsequential in their conversation, more critical, expecially about younger people or any new-fangled systems adopted by the rest of society. Changes like metrification, for instance, are often condemned, even though the rest of society finds it much easier to work in decimals rather than in pounds, shillings and pence. Changes in the language used in church services are even more strenuously resisted by many older people, although not by all.

I do not mean to say that every older person is more rigid, more critical, et cetera, than every younger person. That would be absurd: it is easy to find young people who prefer to measure their height in feet and inches rather than in centimetres; moreover some younger churchgoers are as adamant as older ones in their dislike of change. What I am trying to say is that many of us who were, and are, temperamentally adaptable by nature still find that as we grow older we tend to grumble about change that forces us to realize that we are not as adaptable as we used to be, nor as able to learn as quickly as we did when we were younger. We do not like these diminishments. We often do not like ourselves, and we certainly do not like others in the community when they expose our weaknesses. Being disagreeable and critical offers us a subtle way of revenge. It is easy to vent on others one's anger with one's own frailties, and to become quite cantankerous in old age.

It takes a great deal of courage and humility to admit what is happening and to come to terms with increasing age. If some of us find that we are becoming chronically angry with changes in our community or society we need to do something about it if we are to avoid becoming disagreeable self-opinionated old people. We need to look at the roots of our anger rather than at the triggers that provoke it. Some of these roots are social in origin.

Social Diminishments

One important consequence of ageing is that people often find themselves marginalized in the community. This happens more quickly in some areas of life than in others and at different ages for different people.

Marginalization

It is a fact that many people are seen as "too old" for certain employment when they are scarcely into their fifth decade of life. If these forty-year-olds find themselves "thrown on the scrap heap" they will probably feel rejected. Some of them may even begin to see themselves as failures. Those who are fortunate enough to remain employed until they are sixty-five years old, or older, may also experience themselves as marginal people in the few years before retirement, when they know that others are going to "keep the flag flying" once they themselves have retired or died.

Retired people often feel that they are seen by younger people as objects rather than subjects, people who need help rather than capable of being helpers, people who need to be catered for rather than participants in projects. As many of us grow into real old age we, too, will experience this marginalization and make our responses to its challenge.

Some men and women relinquish their hold of the centre stage relatively easily. They manage to be content to see others taking over where they left off. They are supportive, even pleased to see their successors succeed where they have failed. These are the people who have discovered that although they are no longer important active participants in some project, there are other ways of helping forward the work they want to see done.

Others resist marginalization. They cling to power. They will not give way to younger people. They hang on and on while everyone else waits and tries to tolerate their intransigence. Everyone pays a heavy price when people remain in power once they are no longer capable of supporting the strains and respon-

sibilities of their position. The world watches help-
lessly while the old politicians make serious mistakes
because they are too old for their onerous task.
Employees see their firm's profits decline as they are
forced to wait for a managing director to retire or die
before the necessary reforms can be brought in.
Church congregations see their numbers diminishing
as their eighty-year-old vicar struggles to preach,
teach and visit.

If we find ourselves in power positions before
retirement we may not find it at all easy to know
when to go before we are pushed, when to become
valued repositories of accumulated knowledge and
experience rather than active exectutives. Becoming
marginal to events is never easy. Moreover this
problem is not confined to those in power positions
in society. It can also affect family life, as the
following example shows. I have altered some details
of the story so that no one is identifiable.

When Deanna married John she knew her mother-
in-law as a rather formidable older woman. Mrs
Brown, John's mother, was a competent cook, an
active member of the Mothers' Union and a capable
housewife. Somehow, she made Deanna feel incom-
petent and, worst of all, this feeling was often trans-
lated into reality whenever Mrs Brown came to stay
in the younger Browns' home.

As their children came along, Deanna found that
her mother-in-law's subtle criticism of her manage-
ment of them undermined her confidence and self-
esteem. John continued to be supportive of Deanna's

way of doing things, even though he couldn't understand her reluctance to go and stay with his parents
for weekends and holidays. Nevertheless amicable
relations were maintained until the children were
teenagers. Then disaster struck. John's father died.

By this time Mrs Brown was disabled with chronic
arthritis. John and Deanna talked about Mrs Brown's
future. John was eager to have his mother to live
with them. Deanna was aware of the dangers of this
plan, but she could not see any other solution to their
particular problem. Reluctantly she agreed.

Mrs Brown arrived. Within days she had divided
the loyalties of the children. Within weeks the atmos-
phere at home had become charged with silent tension. Within months Deanna was taking anti-
depressants from her doctor. Two years to the day
from the date of her mother-in-law's arrival Deanna
walked out of her home, leaving a brief note for John
to find.

Everyone in that family suffered from Mrs Brown's
inability to be content to move out of the central
position she had once had in her son's life. The seeds
of this family tragedy were sown during John and
Deanna's engagement, when Mrs Brown had needed
to demonstrate her superiority over her future
daughter-in-law. The bitter fruit ripened over the
years and eventually poisoned all the relationships
within the family.

You may feel that this is an extreme example, and
that John and Deanna should take their fair share of
the blame for the death of their marriage. I am

inclined to agree with you, because I spent part of those two years before Deanna walked out trying to help them to get enough courage and impetus to challenge the old lady. Looking at the situation from outside I could see that the balance between success and failure lay with Mrs Brown's genuine desire to be helpful, together with her inability to cede the centre stage to Deanna, and her fear of becoming a helpless dependant as she grew older.

Happily, this kind of sad outcome is not inevitable. Many older people are content to move from the centre stage to the wings, there to give valued help and support to younger people who have taken over prime responsibility at home, work or in community projects of many different kinds.

If you and I, as we grow older, are to see the dangers of our own reluctance to cede power and help ourselves to retire from leadership roles at the right time, we shall need to be very sensitive to small, yet important, signals from outside, which tell us that it is time to go, to give up, to grow older willingly for the sake of the people or work that one loves and wants to help forward. Judging that moment is one of the hardest tasks that confronts us as we grow older. If we allow ourselves to be marginalized too young we and everyone around us will suffer from our frustration, irritability and tendency to go on interfering: if we leave it too late we ourselves will frustrate everyone else's capacity to build the future on the foundations we laid down during our peak years of endeavour. Then we risk incurring their impatience, contemptuous tolerance and active dislike, which may even turn to hatred.

It is, indeed, true that:

> To know how to grow old is the master work of
> wisdom, and one of the most difficult chapters
> in the great art of living.[14]

Whether people are good judges of when to cede the centre stage or not, there will come a time when they discover that they are no longer fully in control of their choices, for they are beginning to lose their independence.

Loss of independence

As people grow older many of them are likely to find themselves increasingly dependent on younger people. Perhaps they have to give up driving a car: then if they want to go out to far away shops they have to wait until it is convenient for someone else to take them. Perhaps they become too breathless to wash and dress themselves easily: they will need to wait for someone to help them. In the village where I live a high proportion of residents are elderly. Those who are frail or housebound depend on the good will and mobility of those who are younger and still active. Many of them get very used to waiting for other people to come and help them.

Waiting is something we all do throughout our lives. We wait for trains, for buses, for a letter to come through the post to tell us whether or not we have passed an exam. We wait to leave school, find a job, get married. Waiting can be very pleasurable. Many of us wait eagerly for our lovers to phone, or for our spouses to come home and when our waiting is rewarded we are happy. Nevertheless, a lot of our waiting is unpleasant. Few of us enjoy sitting around in a dentist's, doctor's or hospital waiting room, for instance. None of us find waiting for the results of hospital tests for cancer easy. No one could enjoy waiting for an operation, even a simple one. Yet, as you and I grow older we will find ourselves doing more and more of this kind of waiting. Much of that waiting may be quite painful: when, for instance, we have to wait for the expected news of a relative's death, or we begin to wait for a terminal illness to bring our lives to an end.

This kind of waiting has been described in an important book by W. H. Vanstone, *The Stature of Waiting*. In it he highlights what it means to so many people in today's society:

> For an increasing number of people the possibility of a "good life" depends to a considerable degree on the possibility of receiving adequate medical and social support, on the possibility of being watched over and attended to in a diligent and reassuring way . . . It may well be true that the characteristic anxiety of our age is not the anxiety of the young about what they should make of their lives, but the anxiety of the elderly about what will become of them. Certainly the

question "What will become of us?" is often
heard among the elderly people: and it vividly
reflects the speaker's awareness that the satisfac-
toriness of his life at this stage must depend not
so much on what he achieves as on what he
receives, not so much on what he himself does
as on what is done to and for him.[15]

"What will become of us?" is a question which
certainly strikes home when people have to think
about going into sheltered accommodation or an old
people's home. That possibility is a source of anxiety
to nearly everyone who does not wish to become a
burden to his or her children, friends or neighbours.

There are no simple or universal answers to this
dilemma. Some people choose to remain in their own
homes and pay for other people to come in to help,
or even to live on the premises. Some uproot and go
to live near, or with, relatives. Others decide to go
into sheltered accommodation where they can, at
least, maintain a semblance of self-determination.
Many, if they live long enough, will end their lives in
a rest home for old people, or in a nursing home. It
is really very difficult to decide when to take a
particular step towards a sensible disposition of
oneself: people of different temperaments inevitably
make different choices.

Physical health is one important factor in deciding
whether or not to go on living independently. Given
reasonable health, however, one of the other important factors which determine when to exchange inde-

pendence for a measure of dependence on other people is one's ability to face bereavements of all kinds.

Bereavements of all kinds

As people grow older they lose a measure of their physical and psychological strength. They also lose people and places that are important to them.

Many people use the opportunity of retirement to make a fresh start in a new and more manageable home in different surroundings. They do not particularly mind losing contact with former working colleagues, although they are determined to maintain the friendships they made at work and elsewhere. They are still young enough to make new friends in new surroundings. Those who are comparatively young can undoubtedly do that, but, inevitably, as time goes on, they will begin to lose close relatives, helpers and friends, through death, retirement or inevitable change.

Bereavement of any kind is always difficult to come to terms with, but it often becomes crippling to elderly people when it means the loss of close companionship, or the loss of a familiar face or place.

Lovers usually hope to live with each other "till death do them part", meaning to live together till a ripe old age, hoping to die together, or, at any rate, not to outlive the other for very long. Sometimes these hopes are realized, when, for instance, husband and wife are killed in a car crash, or when, as quite often happens, an elderly widow follows her husband to the grave within a few months of his death. Often, however, such hopes are not fulfilled: one partner is left alone at a comparatively early age and while still enjoying relatively good health.

After the initial terrible grief of any bereavement through death, there will usually come a time when the spouse, partner, or close friend, does find it possible to go on alone, even though he or she feels very lonely.

Loneliness may occur at any stage of a person's life, but it undoubtedly increases after the loss of any close relative, lover, partner, friend, child or pet. It increases, too, as one grows older and loses friends, familiar faces and even neighbourhood carers, shop-keepers and shops. Many elderly people, living alone, scarcely see anyone from week to week. They are very reliant on the caring visitor, such as the vicar, community nurse, family doctor, social worker, home help, visiting tradesman or good neighbour. It is a loss when a neighbour moves away. Many elderly people's confidence is undermined when their doctor retires, or hands them over to a younger colleague. When their familiar milkman or postman is replaced by another roundsman it becomes more difficult to ask for the occasional favour. When a pet dies elderly people often lose one of their most important incentives for independence, because having to care for a pet is often a motivating force in old people's lives. While they have to care for an animal, they struggle on: when that animal dies there is often no reason to stay on their own.

I do not want to overstate the problem of loneliness after any form of bereavement. Many old people enjoy living alone. A few prefer their own company to that of anyone else. Many elderly people, however, do not enjoy it, but at the same time, they become fearful and hesitant about asking for help, and also more sensitive to being hurt through thoughtless remarks, indifference and downright neglect. Such people are certainly more prone to bitterness and loss of self-esteem when relatives and friends fail to visit, or neglect to write or telephone when they have promised to do so. "Nobody cares", or, "I keep myself to myself", are words often heard by a doctor making a monthly visit to someone who lives alone.

Paradoxically, the lonelier people become, the harder it seems for them to be able to make positive moves towards becoming less lonely. Professional carers like myself often come across older people who refuse all help and companionship. They will not join a lunch club, go on an outing, visit a day centre, go into an old people's home. They repel visitors, young and old alike. They sometimes refuse access to doctors, nurses, social workers, home helps and neighbours. They become "a problem", even sometimes a neighbourhood "menace" who might, for instance, cause a fire or a flood because of their inability to care for themselves or their homes. Those of us employed as caring professionals to act on behalf of society are often upset when we find someone who isolates himself or herself in this way. We know that it is partly due to our failure to help a client plan for the future at an earlier age and in circumstances where it would have been feasible for that person to make sensible plans about where and how to spend those declining years as enjoyably and safely as possible.

Bereavements of all kinds are hard to bear, especially as people grow older, yet it is not only the loss of people and pets that causes sorrow and hardship. Many people find that they lose their purchasing power and status in society, and that, too, brings much hardship to those who are growing older.

Loss of wealth and status

As I grow older I find myself using my present comparatively high income to prepare for the time when I shall be living on a pension. I expect many people do the same in their pre-retirement years. In an affluent Western society, where people are living longer than those who live in less prosperous parts of the world, many women and men will live many years of their lives as retired people on fixed, or relatively small, incomes. A lot of people nowadays belong to contributory pension schemes which supplement the State benefits. Employers and insurance companies are always urging them to take retirement seriously. Some large institutions, such as the Civil Service, offer pre-retirement courses to their employees, and part of the course is always devoted to money matters.

As a lecturer on health matters at one of our local Civil Service offices, I have been an indirect beneficiary of such courses. Like many other people, I used to put off thinking about the practicalities of the future, and "sufficient unto the day is the evil thereof"[16] had become a kind of watchword for me where money was concerned. Listening one day to another lecturer on the pre-retirement course, one of the problems that had been nagging at the back of my mind for some time surfaced. Recently in our area the Gas Board had offered to lay on a supply of gas to homes like mine which had never before enjoyed the facility. I had humped coal scuttles to feed an efficient anthracite boiler without any difficulty for years. When the offer was first made I saw no reason to spend capital on exchanging one efficient method of heating our home for another. After all, I thought, I was still young enough to do the necessary work and I would feel guilty about spending the money on myself. As I listened to my colleague, however, I changed my mind. I remembered the recent cold winter, the biting wind and the snow. For the first time I saw myself as an older woman, struggling to fill those coal scuttles and dragging them indoors without the strength or breath to manage easily.

I went home and spent the capital. Even now I rejoice in the reduced effort I have to put into this household task, and feel that I have made sensible provision for my old age. Other people may have different priorities. Some enjoy holidays so much that they prefer to struggle with things like coal scuttles, or plan to live very simply for most of the time in order to save up for comparatively luxurious holidays at least once a year. Others prefer music or theatre trips to butter, and are willing to forgo tasty luxuries in order to budget for concerts and outings.

Everyone is different. While there are some people who are temperamentally incapable of retiring, and others who refuse to think ahead, most of us do like to plan for our future. What does seem important in this respect is to make use of any opportunities we have before retirement to take a realistic look at our homes, equipment, economic prospects and present priorities so that we can budget for our future needs.

Self-esteem is often, but not always, linked to purchasing power and status in society. In the West African villages where I worked for a time, older people were considered to be the wisest people in the family or community. They were also seen to be people who could hand down ancestral stories to the younger generation. Their contributions preserved a cohesive and collective tradition in the communities to which they belonged. In Western industrialized countries, however, people tend to lose status as they become older, less affluent, less productive, more dependent. Many of my friends, who are older than I am, tell me that it feels very strange to find that their opinions are no longer taken seriously. They sometimes complain that younger people tend to raise their voices, as if all old men and women were deaf, and speak slowly and carefully to them as if they were now incapable of understanding complex issues. Their opinions are rarely sought. They feel that they are seen by others as recipients of help rather than as potential helpers.

Most people to whom this kind of thing happens laugh and learn to tolerate these unwarranted assumptions: they shrug off the critical and unhelpful attitudes encountered as they grow older. Some react even more positively: they use the negative messages they receive as a spur to help them to prove patronizing younger people wrong. When they band together to form suppport agencies such as Age Concern they can use their considerable electoral power to improve their own life style as well as that of people who are less affluent than themselves.

We do not need to be ashamed of our age. We deserve respect as persons. In our old age we should expect to be treated with dignity and as valued individuals, rather than as despised people who require more help than society is willing to provide. Those of us who are approaching old age, but have not yet arrived, can still do a great deal to ensure that older people are accorded the respect and community support they deserve. We may, for instance, start off by making a few perceptive comments about the abilities of an older person whom we hear being denigrated: we may end up rejoicing in the nomination of an older person to an important committee for some specific cause, possibly even one that is unrelated to older people's problems.

So far I have written about some of the more important physical and psychological problems which people are likely to meet as they grow older. Now, I want to consider some spiritual difficulties.

Spiritual Diminishments

General observations

I am always reluctant to divide persons into separate components labelled "body", "soul" and "spirit": in reality human beings are individuals in whom these three parts are inseparable from birth to death. Whatever happens to our bodies affects our souls, or psyches, and our spirits, by which I mean that part of ourselves which we consider to be our identities, entities which are invisible, intangible and to some extent unknowable, but which seem to transcend the perishable matter of body and mind. Conversely, whatever happens in the depths of our spirits has an effect upon our physical and psychological health.

When I write of the human spirit as if it were a separate part of the whole I am referring to the spirit as a point of entry into the whole person, rather than to a convenient attic into which I can off-load all the rubbish I don't know what to do with, don't need today, but might want to have a look at one day in the future. Although I accept that to many the human spirit seems to be a nebulous concept, I myself believe that it is part of ourselves which enables us to transcend our own egotism and reach out to form relationships, not only with other human beings and creation itself, but also with realities which lie beyond the imminent world of our day-to-day existence.

My own belief in the existence of the human spirit which is a link with other entities, visible and invisible, does not necessarily denote me as a religious person, but it so happens that I am one, I do believe in a Creator whom I name as God, "in whom we live and move and have our being":[17] moreover, I am a practising Christian. It is, therefore, easy for someone like me to attend to the promptings of that part of myself which I call "spirit", which links me to God and to other people. I need, perhaps, to make it clear that I am not equating the "spirit" with conscience, for conscience can be a product of early parental imprinting, but I do think that the spirit sometimes informs our consciences. It may even help some of us to get away from an inappropriate sense of guilt we may have acquired from our parents and other parental figures in infancy or childhood. Although, by and large, I believe it is easier for religious people to think in terms of the spirit than for those who do not believe in God, I do not feel myself to be separate in any way from agnostics and atheists, who also feel accountable in some sense for the way in which we all use the gift of life that we have received.

As I see it, one of the most important functions of the human spirit is to help people to grow away from egotism towards mutuality and interdependence with all that exists. Learning to be sensitive to the needs of other people, and learning to give value to everything that we human beings use or consume during the course of our lives, has been an important part of my own life. As I have grown older I have also grown more sensitive and aware of the way in which I can harm people, animals, plants and matter. I have also developed a greater sense of reverence for everybody and everything with which I come into contact. This awareness and sensitivity is something which seems to happen to many older people, perhaps because we have more experience to reflect on than younger men and women. This increased awareness has important consequences for many of us.

In my work as a deaconess and doctor I have found that many of us who are older brood about things that have happened to us and that we have caused to happen to other people. We find ourselves hurt by what other people have done to us in the past. It seems almost impossible to forgive them. At the same time we know that we, too, often have cause to regret something we have thought or said or done which has caused someone else harm. Sometimes we have been able to put things right. Sometimes we cannot redress the harm we have done: then we have to live with the consequences of our thoughts, words and actions. As we grow older, and have more time for reflection, many of us, I believe, will find ourselves thinking about the past. Our thoughts will challenge us to come to terms with our failures and scars.

Lost opportunities for reconciliation

One of the greatest pains which may afflict us as we grow older may come from a missed opportunity to be reconciled with a parent, relative or friend whom we have hurt or who has hurt us at some time in the past. I have a vivid memory of a small incident that happened when my mother was dying of cancer and I was nursing her.

A few days before she died she was in a lot of pain and had to call for my help repeatedly. On one of these occasions she told me off, just as if I was a small girl again. I reacted with a sulky silence. The moment passed, but neither of us had said "Sorry". As I got into bed I remembered that small incident. "I'll make it up in the morning", I thought, "and I'll ask the doctor to call and see if we can ease her pain more." I fell asleep quite happily.

When I went to see my mother early next morning she had slipped into unconsciousness. The incident had been trivial: at a time of grief, however, it assumed a disproportionate significance and I reproached myself bitterly for my failure to ask her forgiveness. Moreover, to my horror, I found that I wanted her to regain consciousness so that I could get things straight between us. Mercifully for her that did not happen, and she died peacefully three days later.

I can now see the whole of that period in proportion, and I know that such a small unhealed hurt could not mar our strong love for each other, but at the time my grief was increased by remorse, not only for the immediate pain I had caused her, but also for all the suffering we had inflicted on each other during my growing years. My wise husband helped me through this painful experience and waited patiently for me to recover my perspective. It took time, but in the end I found myself healed.

I have found that this small but painful experience of a missed opportunity for reconciliation has helped me to understand some of the suffering that other people have had to endure in similar but rather different ways. I was fortunate in that I could see that the small episode had rekindled some of the deeper unresolved conflicts between my mother and me which dated from the time of my childhood and adolescence. Some of my friends and clients have found it harder than I did to recover buried memories. Some have been unable to forgive or feel forgiven, even when they have remembered what happened to them during their formative years.

Many people seem to get locked into their anger about things that happened to them when they were children. They carry a burden of resentment, bitterness and hidden anger about with them for years. It disrupts their family relationships: often those who carry such burdens try to conceal their true feelings, even from themselves, by pretending to love those whom in reality they hate. When, in later years, they visit their parents, their conversation with each other is full of polite phrases which half-conceal those unexpressed feelings. Parents are often sensitive, not only to what is being said, but also to what is not being said. Sometimes they are able to pick up their children's real feelings for them. They may find themselves afraid to talk about what is happening between them and their children. Individuals in families often wound each other repeatedly because they cannot bring themselves to communicate openly. So when death parts parents and children there is often some unfinished business between them. In that case the children's natural grief may be compounded by regret and remorse.

What has been said about blood relatives applies also to chosen partners and close friends. Disputes happen in every family or close friendship. When a spouse or partner dies suddenly after a squabble, differences of opinion, or a row, the survivor often finds it agonizing to resolve the dispute or quarrel. He or she may accept blame for the partner's death. That guilt may be carried around for a long time, and it sometimes prevents the living person from being able to stop grieving.

Grief that is prolonged by guilt sometimes turns into chronic, self-punitive depression accompanied by agitation, especially as its victims grow older and approach death. Unfortunately, many older people do not realize what is happening to them. They may have forgotten the incident that originally provoked their guilty grief. They may have brushed it aside as irrelevant or pushed it into the recesses of their minds because it was too painful to be remembered. All that they are aware of is a feeling of unrelieved gloom and apprehension. What may look like illness, physical depression or even senility, may in reality be a spiritual problem.

The kind of guilt I have been discussing cannot be cured by pills, E.C.T. or reassurance. It has to be dealt with at a deeper level. This is where it may be wise to call in a priest or pastoral counsellor, someone who is sensitive to the needs of the human spirit. Many older people are greatly helped by interventions which can help them to resolve their conflicts and to forgive themselves for their past sins and errors of judgement. We should not be afraid of turning to such counsellors for assistance, even if they do represent a God in whom we do not believe.

Maybe we who do not die young, but are allowed to grow older, can use the time we are given to heal many relationships that would otherwise have been a source of unhappiness? Certainly, if we find ourselves to be apprehensive about the thought of our own death we may need to look at possible sources of any pain that seems to be linked to self-blame. If we can find the courage to do that, with or without external help, we may be able to find healing for ourselves as well as for those who shared our pain at its source.

Looking back on my own life I find myself grateful for the incident that helped me to look at the unhappiness I had caused my mother, and she had caused me when I was young. Although her death deprived me of the opportunity to tell her what I had learnt, she left me a rich legacy through that moment of dissension between us. Many memories were healed, new insights gained, new understanding of why some people repress such memories rather than endure the strong feelings they might arouse. In short, my mother had given me the means by which I was healed myself and more able to help other people in similar situations and circumstances to find healing for themselves. It has been a rich legacy.

The effects of past failures

The story about my mother's gift to me is told from my point of view, not hers. I cannot know what she thought about in the moments between my leaving her and her sinking into unconsciousness. Knowing her sensitivity, however, I suspect that she will have seen my failure as her own. The incident was so trivial at one level that it may not have caused her more than a moment's sorrow. Had she lived, however, she might have used it, rather as I did, to look back on other failures, not only in our relationship, but also in the rest of her life.

As we grow older it becomes easier to look backwards rather than forwards. We may, indeed, see the past with rose-coloured spectacles so that we deceive ourselves into thinking of them as "the good old days" rather than as the mixture of good and bad that they were in reality. If we take the trouble to listen to ourselves talking about the past we may see ourselves parading "that sign of old age, extolling the past at the expense of the present".[18] If, however, we can avoid that particular trap we may derive much benefit from taking an honest look at some of our past experiences to see what we have learnt from some of our personal failures. Many of us do this during our middle years of life.

Middle age is a dangerous time of life. If people do not recognize and come to terms with their various failures they may find themselves acting in uncharacteristic ways. A lurking sense of failure, for instance, may cause a middle-aged man to discard his wife for a much younger woman who helps him to feel young again. The same sense of failure may induce an executive to throw up a settled position for a "fresh start" in a new profession, or risky enterprise. Sometimes these changes in life style succeed. That half-recognized, or even unrecognized, sense of failure, which prompted a desire for change, is replaced by the kind of self-confidence and happiness that are associated with the increase in self-esteem that comes with success. Sometimes, however, the new life style merely reinforces the sense of failure that underlay the attempt to make drastic changes in order to reach for success.

In writing about the way in which a lurking sense of failure can prompt some men and women to make radical changes in their lives, I do not mean to ignore all the other reasons which can induce people to change direction. I am simply pointing to one important, but relatively little understood, cause of middle-aged discontent which may cause significant alterations in a person's way of life.

Many people pass through this middle-aged restlessness without too much difficulty, and without having to make the kind of changes I have described.

They look back, recognize the failures, balance them with the successes, and get on with life. Other people may not be so fortunate. They may have a considerable struggle to feel that they have accomplished anything worthwhile during their lives. In later middle and real old age these women and men may brood over past events, and be unable to offset their memories of failure with those of success.

One of the early symptoms of this tendency to negative broodiness is the "if only" syndrome, otherwise known as the "what might have been if only . . ." style of thinking about the past, and of our failures in particular. If we find such symptoms creeping up on us we should nip them in the bud, because sterile thoughts about what we might have done, but did not do, are a major threat to happiness and stability in later life.

A modicum of courage, honesty with ourselves, and a realistic appraisal of our lives, should help us to value our failures far more than we are able to do when we were going through those difficult experiences that are associated with failure. Looking back, most of us can see that although we did not do certain things, nor make a success out of certain opportunities, we were able to learn from our mistakes. We did take other directions, sometimes unwillingly, and those paths did bring us happiness. We have managed to survive quite severe setbacks and failures. That ability to survive disaster can strengthen our hopes for the future. After all, if we know that we have lived through one dreadful experience we can at least hope to survive other disasters which life might put in our way.

Once we have conquered any tendency in ourselves to brood over past failures we can cultivate the good habit of being content to live in the present, rather than in the past. We shall be able to build for the future by the way in which we can meet today's claims on our courage.

Self-pity

It is not easy for any of us to grow older. The various diminishments which afflict us seize us in a vice-like clamp and constrain our freedom to use our senses, minds and emotions as we once did when we were younger. Vision may fade, so that we can no longer read small print. Hearing may fail, so that we can no longer enjoy parties or concerts. An impaired memory will make it hard for us to learn new skills. The flattening of our emotions, which is natural to old age, will make it quite difficult for us to engage in enjoyable arguments or to be concerned about some obviously needed social reform which others are eagerly discussing. Those of us who have religious faith often find it harder to concentrate our minds in prayer as we grow older.

At the beginning of these various diminishments we may find ourselves irritated by our various disabilities, but we usually try to overcome them. Later on, however, we may become victims of self-pity, and expect other people to compensate us for our loss of functions, whatever they may be.

During my life as a family doctor I have often encountered old people who were selfish, demanding and miserable to live with because they had become lost in self-pity. Sometimes I found myself very concerned about the relatives with whom these self-pitying people lived. As an illustration I want to describe one typical and not uncommon situation from real life. Mrs Green is not anyone in particular: she is a composite person, drawn from my imagination, but based on real experience.

After years of stubborn independence, Mrs Green stumbled over the frayed edge of a carpet and broke her leg when she was eighty years old. The hospital doctor told her unmarried daughter, Mary, that her mother had a heart condition as well as the broken leg, and that he thought the old lady should no longer live on her own. Without asking anyone else's advice Mary decided to sell up and move in with her mother.

The move was disastrous for them both. The next eight years were the unhappiest of their lives. Mrs Green did not get back on her feet. She became more breathless. Her vision and hearing deteriorated. She stopped being able to enjoy reading, listening to the radio or watching the television. Worse still, she made Mary's life a misery because she wouldn't allow Mary to listen or watch.

"It makes my head hurt", she grumbled, when I challenged her. "I just hear it all as a jumble."

Mrs Green's dependence on Mary grew apace. Before long there were ugly scenes every time Mary wanted to go out. Sometimes the old lady would have one of her "turns", and Mary would be frightened into staying at home. Sometimes Mary would resist the emotional blackmail and go out. Then she would have to face a sulky mother for days on end.

Mary began to hate her mother. She turned to alcohol as a way of helping herself get through each day. Mrs Green screamed critical abuse at her. One day, after a particularly unhappy row, Mary picked up a heavy vase and battered her mother over the head. A neighbour called the police, who called me. I sent the old lady into hospital, and watched a hysterical Mary being taken off to be charged at the police station.

Mrs Green never fully recovered, and died in hospital some months later. Mary's recovery was slow, painful, and complicated by a spell in prison. Eventually, however, she did regain a semblance of health, even though her happiness was always tinged by a certain sadness.

Mrs Green and her daughter were joint victims of the older woman's selfishness and self-pity. Until her eightieth year Mrs Green had been a charming person, much loved by her husband and daughter. Mr Green's death had started a process of decreasing health and increasing dependence, which had culminated in the emergence of unpleasant personality traits which had always been there but had only been exposed by misfortune.

Perhaps this particular tragedy could have been avoided? Perhaps it is an extreme example? Both questions could be answered affirmatively; yet domestic violence between old people and those who have to care for them is not uncommon. Self-pity is only one of the causes of domestic unhappiness, but it is an important one. It is also one of the problems that those of us who are steadily approaching old age can do something about if we are willing to try to curb its more unpleasant manifestations, while at the same time finding the courage to look compassionately at the roots of our self-pity.

It is not easy, but quite possible, to recover from the malaise of egocentric self-pity. Nevertheless, even if you and I do think ahead and manage to conquer some of our more unpleasant character traits, we will inevitably find that, as we grow older and become increasingly dependent on other people, our horizons will diminish. We will have more time to sit and think. We may brood over the past. Uninvited, unpleasant thoughts may assault us. Some of these thoughts may focus on death and what happens to us after death.

Loss of belief in the face of death

In my early middle age I came across one of Arthur Hugh Clough's bold poems. One stanza pulled me up short:

> And almost everyone when age,
> disease, or sorrow strike him,
> Inclines to think there is a God,
> Or something very like Him.[19]

That, I thought, might account for the high proportion of elderly worshippers in the church to which I then belonged. I thought no more about it until I went to live in a village where a majority of its mainly elderly residents never went to church at all. That did not mean that they had no religious faith, nor did it mean that they did not struggle with thoughts about death, and life after death, in much the same way that churchgoers sometimes do. Clough's poem has some truth in it, but it is by no means the whole truth: many people who want to believe in God as they approach the mystery of death find themselves confronting doubt and dark unbelief instead; they have to struggle to hold on to faith in the face of age, disease or sorrow. These struggles are not confined to those who believe but do not go to church: they happen to devout churchgoing Christians as well. Many mature Christians are ashamed of their doubts about the resurrection of the body after death. By this time in their lives churchgoing has become a pleasant habit, a way of meeting friends, combating loneliness and sustaining faith by putting themselves into a climate of faith. They hesitate to discuss their difficulties openly for fear of upsetting others. Instead they embark courageously on a dark journey through the valley of doubt and fear. Their loneliness may be increased by the fact that they worship in the company of those who seem so confident in their beliefs. That kind of dark journey may lead in the end to resurgence of belief as they glimpse the light at the end of the tunnel; but it may not. Some older people will find themselves groping their way through the darkness to the very end of their lives.

All of us, atheists, agnostics, believers, will have some thoughts about death and personal survival after death. We need, I believe, to be less reticent than we commonly are about talking about our fears, doubts and difficulties, hopes, longings and expectations, with other people who are close to us and whom we can trust to be sensitive to our vulnerability as we expose our innermost thoughts.

Speaking personally, as one who has been privileged to discuss death with many older people, I have gained confidence from the simplicity and joy with which many elderly people approach death. I can understand those who say that they long for death, that they are curious to see what happens, that they are eager to dwell closer to God. I can also accept the realism of those who are indifferent about death. They say that if death means annihilation they will not know anything after they die: if death opens a door to a new form of experience they are content to wait for the event rather than try to predict or anticipate what it will be like this side of death. I must confess though that temperamentally I am on the side of those who are, I believe, asked by God to endure doubt. I have been greatly helped by those who have shared their various difficulties with me. Many of them go on their journey through the dark night of doubt and sorrow[20] with courage and hope as their companions. They impart something of that perseverance to me as I follow along behind. Whenever the going gets hard in my own journey I turn to Thomas à Kempis's marvellous passage about trusting God:

> If it be Thy will that I should be in darkness, be Thou blessed; and if it be Thy will that I should be in light, be Thou again blessed. If Thou vouchsafe to comfort me, be Thou blessed; and if Thou wilt have me afflicted, be Thou blessed also.[21]

That idea is itself an echo of the experience that is described in the Old Testament in Job's cry, "Though he slay me, yet will I trust him".[22] An even greater self-abandonment is found in the New Testament, in Christ's words in the Garden of Gethsemane: 'O my Father, if it be possible, let this cup pass from me: nevertheless not as I will, but as thou wilt".[23] Jesus' self-surrender was fulfilled in his great cry of, "It is finished!", as he died on the Cross.[24]

We who are wholly human cannot emulate Christ who was, and is, divine and human, but we can at least try to walk in his footsteps.

The diminishment of death itself

As we approach death we will be stripped of much that we valued when we were younger. Robbed, as it were, of our senses, our strength, our intellect and our independence, we may find ourselves living lives of stark simplicity as we wait for the coming of the merciful release of death. We cannot know what is going to happen to us individually. Looking at very old people, separately or in groups, we may be forgiven if we are sometimes tempted to pray for an early end to our own lives. It is not easy to contemplate some of the indignities and insults that older people sometimes have to suffer. We do not want to see what is happening to them happen to us, or to anyone: yet we often feel helpless and unable to do anything to help them ourselves. It is not death itself that is difficult to face: rather it is a forbidding vision of how we might die that sometimes causes us to shrink from thinking about our own future.

Although many of us do pray for an easy death, most of us will also know that we need to pray for strength to bear whatever lies ahead. Our ability to face old age will depend partly on our own temperaments and partly on the help we receive from God, directly, or through others. Meantime we are provided with many opportunities to learn how to die through the "mini deaths" that happen to us in our lives.

We can meet all our various physical, mental, psychological and spiritual diminishments, such as our need for spectacles, hearing aids, dentures, memory-jogging aids and help from others, in a purely negative way by grumbling and resentment. Alternatively, we can be sensible and thankful for the various aids that improve the quality of our lives. We can be humble about our diminishing memories, and grateful in the right way for the people who help us to make the best use of the intelligence and strength that we still retain. Even the worst of the various "mini deaths" that come to us, such as bereavements, can become an occasion for spiritual growth.

All these different little deaths are a preparation for the dying we will have to undergo before death itself releases us from the bondage of our ageing bodies. We can at least try to practise for this great death by meeting our small deaths with patience and courage.

So far I have concentrated in this book on some of the problems that are likely to come to all of us as we grow older in a healthy way. Ageing is a natural process. As we grow older, however, there is an increased risk that our ageing will be accelerated by illness. These illnesses can threaten our enjoyment of life itself. They can sometimes invade our lives and destroy all pleasure in existence.

In describing some of the more common diseases which can accelerate ageing I have been quite selective, choosing those which can yield to self-help, or which are fairly easy to put right if one has the courage to seek outside help.

Threats to Healthy Ageing

Introduction / Bone & joint illnesses / Breathing
problems / Constipation & digestive troubles /
Heart & circulatory problems / Hormonal problems
/ Mood-related illnesses / Urinary troubles / Sensory
organ problems / Weight & food-related diseases /
The end point of life.

> Since it appears likely I will have indifferent health
> for the rest of my life, must face this quietly and
> gracefully, determine that it shall be the least possible
> worry and detriment to others, and fully used to
> purify a subordinate me to God's will. Steady effort
> to avoid dwelling on own physical state, getting into
> centre of picture and accept the fatigue, monotony
> and humbling details of illness with Joy.[1]

Introduction

Evelyn Underhill was fifty-five years old when she
wrote those words in May 1930. At the time of
writing she was a well-known retreat conductor and
writer. She had one major work, *Mysticism*, behind
her, as well as a host of articles, published lectures
and retreat addresses. She was to write another major
book on *Worship* before she died eleven years later.
She had been staying at a Benedictine abbey for a
time of prayer and reflection, and she jotted down
this resolution at the end of her time there.

Evelyn's resolution was made because her asthma, from which she had suffered all her life, was becoming increasingly bothersome to her. During the remaining years of her life she often found herself prevented from doing what she wanted to do by her breathing difficulties: yet she never allowed the problems to deflect her from her work of writing and being a "soul friend" to a great number of people.

The story of Evelyn's struggle with a chronic and debilitating illness is a record of how a person who is imprisoned by a crippling disease can, nevertheless, use it as a means of self-surrender and abandonment to God's mysterious purposes. In her case the struggle led to a spiritual purification that was reflected in a serenity and joy that was obvious to those who met her for the first time, as well as to those who had been her friends for a long while.[2]

Evelyn Underhill's victory over adversity is probably exceptional. Most of us, including myself, would admit to finding chronic illness or disability so frustrating that we grow more self-centred rather than more selfless and translucently holy as she did. Nevertheless, we see in her life an example of what can be done, even if we know we cannot fully emulate it in our own lives. In our own different circumstances we too can meet some of the diseases that commonly attack older people, in ways which help us to become more whole than we were before we fell ill.

This is not a text-book of gerontology, and I have no intention of writing at length about every degenerative disease which can afflict older people, but I do want to refer to some of the more common illnesses that befall those who are growing older. These illnesses cause disabilities which threaten a person's enjoyment of life. Since many of them are the direct result of ageing they cannot always be avoided or cured but they can be managed sensibly.

Bone and Joint Illnesses

As we grow older very many of us will suffer from some form of bone disease or arthritis.

Osteoporosis

When people are young and healthy their bones are strong and well calcified. One of the consequences of growing older is that the bones lose some of their calcium and become less dense. This condition, known as osteoporosis, causes the bones to become more brittle, which is why older people's bones fracture more easily than do those of younger men and women. If older people trip over a rug, miss their footing on a high kerb, or fall off a stool when they are trying to reach for something on a high shelf, the chances of their ending up with a broken hip or leg bone are greatly increased.

If you and I are to avoid such disasters, and a broken hip or thigh bone is a catastrophe to anyone who is older, we will need to be careful where we put our feet when we are walking, running, climbing steps or going downstairs. We need to do everything we can to prevent ourselves from falling. This means wearing sensible shoes with well repaired heels, as we are more likely to stumble and fall if the heels are worn down on one side or the other. It means having something handy to grab hold of if we are trying to reach up for something on a high shelf, or standing on a step ladder or chair, because as we grow older we are prone to dizziness when we have our arms up above our heads. Spending money on a good set of steps is a wise investment if it is going to prevent us from ending up in hospital with a broken leg or arm. As we approach old age we may need to get a firm grip on our pride and decide to buy the most sensible and best looking walking sticks we can get hold of, so that when we go out for a walk on hilly or uneven ground we can do so with confidence. We need to watch the ice and snow from the safety of a warm room. If we do have to go outdoors in such inclement weather we will be wise to go armed with good boots, crampons, a stick and preferably someone else to hold on to as well.

All this is common sense but it is remarkable how often such measures are ignored. Moreover, many people's homes are potential death traps. As soon as we retire, and at regular intervals afterwards, we need to go round our houses looking for curled up edges of carpets and dangerous obstacles over which we might trip and fall. It is surely better to discard a hall rug, or nail it firmly to the floor, than to risk stumbling over it in the middle of the night. It is better to ask a local Social Services department to come and put up an extra stair rail to hold on to as we go downstairs than to fall on our way down to breakfast. It is also sensible to ensure that stairways, halls and rooms are well lit, and that our grand-children's toys are not left all over the floor where we can stumble over them.

This, too, is common sense. Unfortunately it is well known that as people grow older they are less likely to be observant about hazards than they were in youth and middle age. It is, therefore, important for us to make the necessary changes in our homes and ways of living *before* we reach old age, *before*, rather than after, we have fallen and hurt ourselves. It also means that if we ourselves are looking after elderly relatives we will need to see what we can do to ensure that their living conditions are as safe as possible. We need not be obtrusive about it, but we may save them a great deal of suffering if we can make their homes and gardens safer places for them to enjoy.

Joint problems and osteoarthritis

Brittle bones are one problem. Stiff joints are another. As people grow older the ends of the bones, where they join each other, become roughened. The joint spaces between the bones tend to become narrower. This means that sometimes two bones grate on each other as the joint bends instead of being cushioned by a good layer of fluid in the joint space between the bones. The joints creak. They may also protest.

As we grow older many of us will find it less easy to sit cross-legged on the floor, or to get up from a low armchair, than we did when we were younger. Some of us will also find that the movements of some of our joints are painful, especially in the early morning when we are moving them for the first time after our night's sleep. It becomes a real effort to get out of bed. Our hands don't grip the kettle we need to fill for the early morning cup of tea we want to drink. We may find that we can no longer knit, sew, mend fuses or repair broken china and furniture as easily as we used to. Backache may become a familiar companion, and turning our heads quickly an impossibility.

This kind of joint disease that many of us will suffer from is called osteoarthritis. It is a different condition from the joint disease known as rheumatoid arthritis, which more usually affects younger people. Osteoarthritis is always unpleasant. It can be disabling but is generally less crippling than severe rheumatoid arthritis, where the ends of the affected bones get dissolved and absorbed as well as roughened.

Osteoarthritis is responsible for a great many problems in older people's lives, especially where important joints, such as those in spine, hips, wrists and fingers, are involved, for we use those joints every time we move around. Moreover, the joint problems are often compounded by accompanying muscular weakness, or wasting, which renders the joints less stable and makes movement even more difficult.

Osteoarthritis is always a nuisance. Sometimes it is

much more than that: chronic arthritis can be very painful. It is no fun at all, for instance, to live with a painful hip which protests all day long and won't even let its owner get a peaceful night's rest. Loss of mobility can lead to other difficulties too, for digestive troubles and constipation are more common in those who cannot move about easily. People's hearts and lungs also tend to suffer if they are confined to a chair, or to bed, for any length of time. In one sense, osteoarthritis is not curable: yet its symptoms can be abolished altogether in some people and alleviated in others by all kinds of treatments, from hot baths to the use of sophisticated drugs and high technology joint replacement surgery.

If you have osteoarthritis you need not despair. You can help yourself by remaining as mobile as possible. You can improve your mobility by keeping your joints warm, and by doing exercises to strengthen the muscles surrounding the joints. You can obtain simple, safe pain killers from your family doctor. You can try acupuncture, copper bracelets and special diets, all of which are much safer than powerful drugs, and, it has to be said, sometimes just as effective. You should not give up just because you may not find an instant cure at your first attempt.

You will need a modicum of good fortune and a more substantial amount of perseverance to combat this disease. You may need to make contact with your Social Services department. Social workers can supply practical help such as someone to help you with your housework, or a hot midday meal. They can also put you in touch with someone who can supply you with devices to help you open screw-top jars, turn door handles, pick up small objects from the floor, write more easily or eat more comfortably. Do not be slow to ask for the help you need and have a right to have. It may not be offered without your asking for it, but it is there and can be found if you are prepared to go on looking for it.

Doctors and surgeons will always want to help you, but at the same time they will want to avoid using the kinds of powerful drugs and surgical intervention that may do more harm than good in the long run. They do not always jump at the chance of using the latest "wonder drug", or offer you the kind of treatment that you might have read or heard about from the media. Nevertheless they can do a great deal to help, but it has to be admitted that they will sometimes need pushing before they come up with the answer to your particular problem. This is because some treatments are risky, and it is not justifiable to use them unless the patient cannot be helped in any other way. Unfortunately there are a few occasions on which a client may be told, "There's nothing more we can do to help you: you'll have to learn to live with the problem". These are dreadful words for anyone to hear: clients who refuse to accept such statements may do humanity a great service by their searches for cures to conditions that are presently deemed incurable.

Breathing Problems

As men and women grow older their lungs tend to lose elasticity, and their hearts cannot pump the blood round the body as efficiently as when they were younger. The result is that many older people get breathless when they hurry or exert themselves more than usual. Some people who are used to getting around at a brisk pace will find that they need to stop after a comparatively short distance, not because of pain but simply because they are puffing and wheezing. Some may even find that they need to sit down with their arms resting on a table in front of them if they are to recover their breath easily. Being breathless isn't necessarily a sign of serious lung or heart disease, but it is a symptom that needs to be evaluated by a family doctor.

If you find yourself getting more breathless, either on effort, or, perhaps, in the middle of the night when you find yourself wanting to sit up and cough, you need to get yourself checked out by a doctor just in case there is something important behind that symptom. The doctor may be able to help you more than you think. In many cases common sense supplies the answer to many simple breathing problems in older people: you will be told to slow down, but keep moving; stop smoking if you possibly can; make sure you are not overweight; use a couple of extra pillows at night if you find that comfortable, because heart and lungs both work more efficiently if you sleep high.

Such measures are often effective for a long time. After the initial consultation you may not need to see your doctor very often. You should, however, always consult your family doctor if something new happens, such as a change in the colour and quantity of your sputum, or increased breathlessness.

Anyone who has chronic bronchitis, or some circulatory trouble like high blood pressure or heart disease, is going to get a bit worse as he or she gets older. It becomes harder to cough up sticky sputum. The ageing heart finds it harder to keep the blood pumping smoothly to the lungs where it can absorb oxygen. The lungs are less efficient so they don't allow the oxygen to filter into the blood as well as they should, and the result is that no part of the body, including the brain, gets the blood supply it deserves. However, you should never consider yourself too old to ask for medical help. Happily, scientific knowledge and modern medicines have revolutionized the treatment of lung and heart diseases, and the prognosis is good for many people.

Constipation and Digestive Troubles

Constipation causes problems for many older people. The bowel muscles lose their elasticity. Abdominal muscles become flabby. Few elderly people drink enough fluid during the day, so the bowel contents tend to solidify. In consequence they find themselves struggling to evacuate the contents of their lower bowel. Many older people become blocked up altogether. Others make themselves ill by taking increasingly large quantities of laxatives to keep their bowels open. The fact is that the whole digestive tract slows down as people grow older. They do not generally need to worry if they do not have their bowels open every single day. At the same time it is true that defaecation needs to be as effortless as possible, because excessive straining can put an extra load on an old person's heart and lungs.

Good bowel care for anyone of any age depends on a high fibre diet, a good fluid intake and adequate exercise. Unfortunately many of us tend to eat less fibre rather than more as we grow older, partly because our teeth don't chew as well as they used to, partly because we are afraid of becoming "windy". Cheerful doctors who tell us to eat loads of bran, cabbage, baked beans and brown bread are right in their advice, but sometimes insensitive to the reasons for our reluctance to comply with their suggestions. Porridge and a glass of brown ale at night might be more acceptable. If you find yourself afflicted with constipation, or, as often happens, by alternating constipation and diarrhoea, please vary your diet and exercise before you rush to the medicine cabinet. All laxatives other than bran and fibre contain substances which can be harmful if taken in large quantities or continuously. Try not to be upset if you do lose control over your "wind" or find your underclothes stained occasionally. Chronic faecal incontinence can be very distressing to many people and to their relatives. It is always worth while asking for help from the community nursing services. It is also wise to consult your family doctor if you find your bowel habit changing; if, for instance, you find yourself persistently loose when you're usually constipated, or pass blood on any occasion. If you do have to take laxatives it is always worth asking your doctor for the safest brand.

Constipation is a very common ailment among older people. Indigestion is less common but just as distressing. Heartburn, acid regurgitation and unpleasant "burping" are uncomfortable and upsetting. It is not surprising that old people's bathroom cabinets are often full of different proprietary medicines which have been tried out at one time or another. Other strategies may be more effective and less dangerous. Many elderly people, for instance, will find it helpful to take small frequent meals and to cut down on their tea and coffee intake. All can benefit from weight reduction if they are obese. It is wise to try these strategies before taking medicine, and you should stop taking medicines if they cease to work or have to be taken in increasing quantities to achieve symptomatic relief. If either of those things happen you should consult your family doctor. Similarly, if the symptoms worsen despite initial success, or if they change in character or are accompanied by other symptoms, like vomiting or bleeding, you should seek medical help.

Heart and Circulatory Problems

Most of us will get some kind of heart trouble or circulatory disorder if we live long enough to grow really old. Heart and artery muscles share the general tendency of all muscles to grow weaker as people grow older. The circulation slows down. Arteries may lose their elasticity, or get clogged up, and people may find themselves in trouble, with symptoms such as angina, cold blue feet and/or cuts that do not heal properly. Some may find themselves suffering from dizzy attacks, sudden loss of consciousness and even strokes.

Circulatory problems are relatively easy to understand if you think about what might happen if any part of your body was to be suddenly deprived of its blood supply, or the heart pump were to become less efficient. People are right to be afraid of circulatory problems, because serious heart disease, very high blood pressure, strokes, gangrene of the toes, or perhaps sudden loss of sight in one or both eyes through a blocked retinal artery or vein, can spell disaster for their health and destroy their ability to enjoy being alive.

Most of us know what can happen to us as we get older. Many of us naturally pray to be spared the suffering we see other people having to endure, but at the same time we also hope that we and our families will be able to cope if we fall victim to an unpleasant circulatory illness. That seems to me to be a sensible attitude to adopt, provided that we are also astute enough to do what we can to prevent ourselves from getting into more trouble than we need. Again, the principles of healthy living apply. In this instance they are important, not only as we grow older, but also throughout our lives. Nevertheless, even if we have neglected our health when we were younger, we can still do something about it as we grow older.

If your heart and arteries are to keep working efficiently for as long as possible, you need to take plenty of unhurried exercise, such as walking, playing bowls or enjoying ballroom dancing. You should reduce your intake of animal fat, eat as much fibre as you can enjoy, drink alcohol in moderation and keep your weight down. Smoking is always harmful to your health. Refuse to get overstressed. Stop pretending that you are as young as a gazelle and take time to do what you want to do, and to rest when you want to. Keep your body warm and look after your precious feet, for this is where the cold, together with the poor circulation, can cause ulcers, swollen blue toes and loss of mobility.

Remember that it is normal for your blood pressure to be higher when you are older, and spare yourself from needless anxiety about it. Remember also that natural loss of arterial elasticity will mean that you will not tolerate sudden drops in your blood pressure as well as you did when you were younger. Many elderly people find that if they try to work with their arms above their heads for any length of time they get dizzy, because the blood tends to rush to their feet. The same happens if they straighten up after bending down, or get up suddenly after sitting or lying down for a while. So you and I will make life a great deal safer for ourselves if we think ahead and plan our homes and lives in such a way that we will be able to avoid keeping things that we need most often either too high on our shelves or too low in awkward-to-get-at cupboards. Forethought and good planning, based on sound principles, can do more to keep us healthy in our old age than visits to our doctor's surgeries or hospital clinics can ever do for us once we have become ill, especially if those illnesses could have been prevented through sensible measures. Unpreventable catastrophes and diseases are another matter altogether, and no one should feel guilty if he or she is unfortunate enough to fall victim to those sorts of disasters and illnesses.

Hormonal Problems

Certain important organs in the body, such as the thyroid, pancreas, liver, kidney and sexual organs, tend to stop producing important hormones as they grow older. Consequently it is not unusual for older people to suffer from conditions like hypothyroidism, sugar diabetes, impotence, frigidity and vaginitis. Diseases of the hormone-producing organs are tedious to have to put up with, because when a gland stops producing hormones it does not recover. The only way of helping someone who lacks thyroid, or who cannot produce insulin or sex hormones, is to replace the absent hormone by substitute hormones, extracted from dead people or other animals, or by the manufacture of synthetic substances. In that event the treatment will have to continue every day for the rest of the person's life.

There is a lot of discussion in medical circles about replacement hormone therapy for menopausal and post-menopausal women. Daily replacement therapy can alleviate the unpleasant symptoms that menopausal women often suffer from, such as hot flushes, swinging mood changes and dry vaginitis; it will also prevent or postpone the onset of osteoporosis that predisposes older people to fractures. There are, however, disadvantages and dangers to such prolonged treatment, and close monitoring of every woman taking such hormone replacement therapy is essential. Decisions about the suitability of this kind of treatment for a particular woman should always be taken on an individual and trial basis, and never without a good doctor's help. We are fortunate to be living in an age when so much can be done to help people who are suffering from these kinds of problems.

Mood-related Illnesses

By the time we are approaching retirement many of the mood-related problems of middle age, such as the menopausal mood swings in women, or the "roving eye" syndrome in men, have passed, or at least become less insistent. Late middle age and early old age can be pleasurable periods of life when people tend to be relatively stable, yet are still active and productive. This means that some women and men find that there are as many pleasures to growing older as there are difficulties, at any rate during their early years of retirement. A friend, speaking about this period of her life, comments on some effects of ageing on her mood and sees how loss in one direction can become gain in another. She speaks about her diminishing ability to engage in activities, meetings and gatherings that once gave her pleasure, and then adds:

> But with these losses a great deal of the "clutter" of life falls away too. Living becomes much more of a pure gift which is felt and valued with infinite gratitude each day. The company of friends and the amazing beauty of creation as the seasons come and go become more deeply felt. Gratitude to God seems the outstanding and spontaneous daily prayer. HE has been giving me so much all through my life, and I am only now just beginning to really SEE. Imperceptibly the active life grows into the contemplative.
>
> I would say that the early years of old age can be among the best of one's life – they are the golden years, lived intensely to the full.[3]

As people grow into old age, however, the balance between pleasure and pain changes. Older people are more prone to anxiety and depression as they see their strength ebbing away and have to let go of many of the relationships and activities they enjoyed so much when they were in the prime of life. Many people find themselves irritated by their forgetfulness, anxious about change, depressed by misfortune or bereavement.

Grief-related illnesses

Grief after severe bereavement of any kind, usually the death of a spouse or other close relative, but sometimes the loss of employment, status or a precious home, is not itself an illness, although those who are newly bereaved often feel dreadfully ill because of physical symptoms such as loss of appetite, excessive fatigue, poor concentration, sudden uncontrollable mood swings, guilt ruminations, daytime hallucinations, mental confusion and severe insomnia. These are all normal symptoms, and newly bereaved people need a great deal of understanding and help during the first months and years of their traumatic experience. Although the symptoms of grief do not imply an individual is ill, bereavement can precipitate illness.

The signs that someone is becoming ill with a grief-related disease are not always easy to detect, but include worsening of symptoms over a period of time, deepening of guilt feelings and delayed recovery of functional ability. People who are usually quite stable find themselves ill with phobia, anxiety and depression. Mood-related illnesses are not only due to grief, of course, but bereavement is an important precipitating factor in such illnesses among older people, especially among those who have never before suffered from phobia, anxiety or depression.

Whatever the cause or precipitating factor, the consequences of having a mood-related illness are serious for many older people. Such illnesses can be devastating to people's lives, sanity and self-esteem. Men and women who find themselves afraid, agitated, depressed or both, are often ashamed of their state, even though there is no need for shame of any kind. Although I am writing about phobia, agitated depression and profound depression as though they are different conditions, I should point out that there is considerable overlap in their symptoms.

Phobias

Phobias are not confined to any particular age range. Young and old victims can be found everywhere. Some people become afraid to get shut into lifts; others fear travelling on buses, or become unable to use tube escalators. Some become afraid of germs, and spend their time cleaning house and washing their hands or cooking utensils. Certain phobias are, however, common among older people, and one of the worst of these, from the older person's point of view, is agoraphobia.

Many older people begin to find themselves reluctant to go out of the house, especially alone. They may justify staying at home by reference to the dangers of being mugged, or they may be able to admit to irrational fear. Gradually the "stay at home" attitude begins to prevail. Self-confidence is lost and it becomes harder to go out. The vicious circle has begun to be operative. In certain circumstances an elderly woman or man who seldom goes out, never socializes, or rarely sees anyone to talk to, may develop full blown agoraphobia and become quite unable to go out at all.

Phobias have nothing to do with defects in personality or lack of will power. They rarely yield to determination, other people's bullying or contempt. They need not, however, dominate or decimate a person's whole life. They can be treated. In general it is easier to help phobic people at an early stage of the problem rather than later, when the condition is well established. If, perchance, you find this kind of problem insinuating itself into your life, be quick to seek proper outside help.

Agitation and agitated depression

Agitation is different from irrational fear. Many older people become agitated if they have to do anything that is different from their normal routine. It becomes difficult to meet new people, go into a new shop or tackle tasks they could have easily accomplished when they were younger. They may become depressed because they are anxious and agitated since they find themselves so gloomy.

Agitated depression is not at all uncommon among elderly people. The depression is often masked by the anxiety and restlessness which are so predominant in this condition. The victim cannot settle to anything. He or she paces up and down the home, fusses about every little thing that goes wrong, and becomes very difficult to please. Someone who is suffering from this condition often becomes hypochondriacal or preoccupied with themselves. It may be impossible to convince them that they are physically healthy.

People who suffer from agitated depression do not get better with reassurance or tranquillizers. They do get better when the depression is adequately treated. The diagnosis is not always easy to make and should, therefore, be thought of in anyone who is very agitated or anxious without cause.

Profound depression

Depression can also occur without agitation. People who are afflicted by a depressive illness often find that they no longer enjoy eating, seeing friends, or going out. They often sleep fitfully, wake in the middle of the night and then cannot go back to sleep again. When morning comes they feel miserable, and it becomes difficult to get up and start moving about. They may fall victim to brooding over past mistakes and faults, become guilty and even feel unworthy to receive any help. Occasionally they may become paranoid and feel the whole world is against them, or suffer from delusions that their children, friends or even professional carers hate them and are plotting to kill them.

Depressed people may turn to alcohol or sleeping drugs for relief from their symptoms: in time they may become alcoholics or drug-dependent. There are, of course, many other reasons for alcoholism among the elderly, which is not an uncommon condition, but mood-related problems are among the commonest reasons for an old person turning to the bottle of cheap whisky or sherry to find oblivion from their problems.

Depression is a terrible condition for anyone to suffer. It is doubly hard on older people, who cannot find the physical strength to "work it off" as younger people can sometimes do. Some elderly victims may find that the depression becomes so profound that they cannot find the energy to feel agitated or want to get better. Instead, they sit in their chairs or lie awake at night, mute with misery, overwhelmed with guilt, longing to die. Suicide attempts are uncommon at this stage of the illness, but they are quite common during the period when the victim feels they are going into this kind of profound unhappiness, or, paradoxically, when they are beginning to come out of the depths of their dreadful experience.

I have described the worst that can happen, but the worst need not happen. If, as you grow older, you do find that mood changes are beginning to become a problem, try not to let them get a hold of your life. Try to get help quickly. Some of the best kind of help can come from increased contact with family, friends, a kindly doctor, community nurse or social worker. Sometimes the best kind of help will come from inside yourself. If you can still see that there are people in the community and society who are worse off than you, then you may be able to regain your balance by doing something to help other people. If you are reasonably healthy from a physical point of view your help may be welcomed and valued at the local lunch club, church or charity shop. You may find yourself able to help others who are more handicapped than you are. Even if you are house-bound, you may find that you can stave off phobia, anxiety and depression by encouraging yourself to look after a pet, knit for a charity, write letters to lonely people, collect stamps for the local church, or find another absorbing interest.

If, on the other hand, you are a relative or carer for someone who is "shut in" or sunk in unhappiness, you may have to fight your way through the wall of their depression, guilt or paranoia that so often causes an older person to refuse any help that is proffered. You will certainly have to be alert to the possibility that the mood changes in the elderly person you are caring for may be related to alcohol or drugs. Early morning and evening confusion, frequent dizziness and falls, slight but variable slur-ring of speech, sudden euphoria, loss of appetite and weight, and chronic diarrhoea are the symptoms which you should take seriously enough to want to enquire about, and make sure that alcohol and drugs are not their cause.

Looking after elderly and very old people is no sinecure. You may have to wait for a long time before the elderly person you are caring for seems to respond to any overtures of friendship or suggestion you may make. You will have to earn their trust the hard way. You may fail, but you will never have any success at all if you are put off by those walls of fear, guilt and hostility that imprison so many old people.

Some of the richest rewards of being a family doctor came to me from my weekly or monthly contacts with elderly people in the neighbourhood where I worked. Banging on their doors, listening to their grumbles, persuading them to accept visitors or help, refusing to go away when they told me off, was hard work, but the rewards and satisfactions of seeing old people regain their sense of joy in life and their self-esteem were high too. In an ageing population, such as we have in Britain today, it will be increasingly important to have both younger and not so young people in the community who are willing to visit elderly and infirm people, go on visiting them and encouraging them to enjoy their old age in all kinds of ways.

Urinary Troubles

Stress incontinence in women and prostatic obstruction in men are two common and distressing conditions which afflict many older people.

Stress incontinence

Stress incontinence is so common in women who have had children that many of them do not think of it as an illness at all. They know that they are going to leak urine when they cough, laugh, carry heavy shopping or cannot reach a toilet quickly enough when they feel the urge to pass water. Many women simply carry spare underclothing with them wherever they are and get on with their lives as best they can. Stress incontinence is always a nuisance. It often becomes intolerable when it is accompanied by vaginal prolapse or becomes so frequent that it amounts to a continuous dribble.

Weight reduction, pelvic floor exercises, frequent bathing and changes of clothes can do much to alleviate the unpleasant side effects of this condition. A relatively simple operation can be done to correct any accompanying prolapse and/or sling up the bladder, so that it doesn't press on and weaken the urinary sphincter. This can cure some kinds of urinary incontinence and it is always worth thinking about such an operation if you have this problem and are relatively young and not too overweight.

Prostatic obstruction

Prostatic obstruction is common in older men. Many men who are over sixty years old will have some difficulty starting micturition or passing a good stream of urine whenever they want to. They may also find that they are dribbling a little at the end of micturition. The enlarged prostate sometimes causes irritation to the bladder: this means that many men find they have to get up several times a night to pass small quantities of urine. Some men are unfortunate enough to become obstructed, and then find themselves unable to pass any water at all. If this happens suddenly it is very painful: a patient will inevitably and, as it happens, most fortunately, have to seek medical help at once, thus getting the necessary treatment speedily. If the condition of urinary retention comes on more slowly there may be very little pain in the run-up-time to the retention, but there will be much back pressure up through the ureters to the kidneys. The bladder and ureters become enlarged, the kidneys diseased. The end result of untreated chronic prostatic enlargement may be renal failure.

Most prostate troubles are due to a simple non-malignant enlargement of the prostate gland, but cancer of the prostate can affect older men. Initially the symptoms are similar to those of the less serious condition, so any urinary symptom in men needs to be carefully evaluated. Difficulty in starting to pass water, frequent visits to the toilet at night, or dribbling of urine should always be taken seriously by older men. So should the passage of blood of any kind or quantity. The treatment of all prostatic diseases and most bladder disorders is now effective and generally successful in the long run.

The kidneys wear out as people grow older, so

people sometimes get into trouble through renal failure, as they age. In its early stages this condition can only be diagnosed by special tests. This is one of the reasons why some doctors advocate regular check-ups for all older people.

Urinary incontinence, hesitancy in passing water, or retention of urine are embarrassing conditions. Older people often hesitate to seek medical advice. If you find yourself in more than very slight difficulty, however, if micturition becomes painful at any time, or if your urine goes a different colour, you need good medical advice, and you will not be bothering your family doctor unnecessarily if you seek it.

Sensory Organ Problems

Cataracts, glaucoma, retinal haemorrhages and progressive deafness are common problems in older people. Most people have a natural dread of becoming blind or deaf.

Visual diseases

Many women and men worry about their eyes and ears long before they wear out. On being told she had cataracts one of my friends remembers walking down a road seeing everything with a new intensity:

I look back and remember stopping on the road out of Cambridge, saying to a friend, "Let's

always remember this turn in the road, these
fields and hedges and these glorious open spaces
and the sky."[4]

It may be small comfort to a patient to know that she
or he may die before the cataract is dense enough to
cause blindness, but it is quite often true. It is also
true, however, that no one is ever too old to have a
cataract operation: many people have had useful
sight restored to them in extreme old age.

Glaucoma is a condition where the pressure of the
fluid in the eyeball builds up because it cannot escape
through the natural channels as it should. Glaucoma
may produce pain in the eye or sudden deterioration
in vision. Loss of vision may be preceded by the
appearance of coloured lights and haloes in the visual
field, and this is a useful warning signal, but only in
some people. Glaucoma may cause blindness. It is
curable in most cases, either through the use of
special drugs and eye drops or through surgery. Older
people are always wise if they get into the habit of
having regular check-ups with an optician, because
this is one of the best ways of finding the condition
before it does real damage to the eyesight.

The blood vessels at the back of the eye sometimes
bleed or become blocked. When something like that
happens, or the retina, the seeing part of the eye,
becomes detached, the patient may suddenly lose
sight, partially or completely, in one or both eyes.
Such an event is a disaster for anyone, and many
older people who are unfortunate enough to develop

these conditions have to learn to live with considerable disabilities.

Auditory diseases

The kind of progressive deafness that affects many older people, usually called sensori-neural deafness, is not curable, but people's residual hearing can often be improved by the use of a hearing aid. Modern hearing aids are small and effective. If you think you are deaf and might need an aid you would be wise to seek advice from an accredited specialist initially, rather than buying an aid through an untried source, as the causes of deafness are complex. Your precise needs will require careful evaluation if you are to receive the best aid for your particular condition.

If you are one of the people who is experiencing difficulties about your sight, hearing, taste, smell or other sensory organ as you get older, do not immediately think about the worst that could happen. If you approach your problem with an optimistic mind and get a good specialist opinion, and a second one if you are not satisfied with the first one, you will find that a great deal can be done to help you.

Weight and Food-related Diseases

I have left weight problems and food-related diseases to the last, not only because they are the last alphabetically, but also because obesity has been a serious hazard to my own health and the one I least like thinking about: however, it has to be done because obesity kills.

Obesity

Obesity complicates and compounds all the other problems that people encounter as they grow older, except, perhaps, that of constipation. Men and women who are overweight are more likely to become ill with heart troubles and breathing difficulties than those who are close to their ideal weight. They have an increased risk of developing arthritis, diabetes, high blood pressure, hiatus hernia and prolapse of the uterus. They have increased complication rates and mortality rates after surgical operations compared with people of normal or near normal weight.

It is easy to see why obesity is so dangerous to older people. It is far less easy to reduce and stay slim than most doctors will admit. "Eat less", they say irritably, "and you'll lose weight." That statement is true, but many older people, who burn up less energy than they did when younger, have to reduce their calorie intake so drastically in order to lose weight that it is not surprising that few people enjoy the thought of living on a low calorie diet for long periods of time.

Like many fat people I have been able to stick to a reducing diet at periodic intervals with considerable determination, but like most I have frequently relapsed after reaching an acceptable weight level. Now that I am getting older, however, an instinct for self-preservation is beginning to take hold of my life more successfully. I certainly do not want our children to have to heave me about like a sack of coal were I to become wheelchair bound or bedridden. That fate may never befall me, but if it does I mean to be ready for it. Good motivation strengthens resolve. Improved health is an effective spur to self-control, particularly if relatives and children are included in one's good intentions.

Obesity is never easy to tackle, even if people have a good motivation and strong will power. If, like me, you are afflicted with overweight problems as you grow older, you may find it helpful to make your diet more interesting by varying it on a rotation basis. Reducing diets need not be expensive; they can be quite fun, but they do need to be well balanced. There are plenty of books and magazines which give good information on diets and their content, but sometimes the most effective way of slimming is to seek outside help from a local community dietician or reputable slimming club. Week by week monitoring, together with support and encouragement, help to keep many people on their diet. Such measures do not suit everyone. Some of us find that we have to diet in secret because outside scrutiny and comment, whether they are positive or negative, has the weird effect of inducing us to eat more. We are all individuals in this matter and simply need to know ourselves and to find any method which is effective for us, irrespective of whether or not it helps other people.

In stark contrast to Third World countries, where more people will die from starvation than from over-indulging in food, obesity is the most common weight problem to be found in highly industrialized countries like Britain. It is not, however, the only problem that older people may have to face, for many elderly people grow thinner, and develop muscle wasting, as they grow older, even though they are not suffering from any particular disease.

Anorexia

Old people's appetites tend to dwindle when the smell and taste of food become more difficult to appreciate, and when chewing is less easy to accomplish. Many elderly people find that it is too much effort to cook food and wash up dishes, particularly if they live alone. If they are housebound they do not get the stimulus of seeing what is available at their local shops. Many elderly people find themselves lacking the desire or energy to make use of lunch clubs or "meals on wheels": gradually they stop eating healthy food, and begin to rely on convenience foods and things like tea and bread and butter that are relatively easy to prepare. This is a recipe for disaster, and if you find yourself in this kind of situation as you grow older you should try to get out of it as quickly as you can.

Whether we are vegetarians or omnivores, fibre or

health food addicts, too fat, too thin, or "just right", we all need to appreciate that a healthy, balanced diet is just as important for older people as it is for children and younger people. When we are older we do not need to eat as much as we did when we were younger, but we do need to take care to see that the balance of protein, carbohydrate and fat in our diet is right. This is much more important than stuffing ourselves with expensive vitamins and mineral pills, or spending money on alcohol or cigarettes instead of food. Local health education councils, community dieticians and nurses and family doctors often keep helpful literature on diets and general health care for the elderly. These, and good advice, are usually readily available if you ask for them.

Alcoholism

One food-related problem which few of us like thinking too much about, but which afflicts many older people, concerns the use and misuse of alcohol as a food. Alcohol is a convenience food, being high in calorie content, easy to take and assimilate, and, initially at any rate, an easy source of energy. It is also socially acceptable, often valuable as a way of making outside contacts. Going to the pub, or having friends round for a party, can be a pleasant and healthy activity. Unfortunately alcohol is also a mood elevator for some people and a tranquillizer for others. It has some dangerous side effects, especially for older people.

Solitary and secret drinking, which is more danger-ous than social drinking, often begins in older people when they find that alcohol helps them to get to sleep after a bereavement, or that it acts as a mild pain killer or helps them to forget their troubles and blots out anxiety. Their use of alcohol in such circumstan-ces is understandable. Moreover, doctors often advo-cate the use of alcohol for people with mild heart problems, anxiety and post-bereavement insomnia, so solitary drinkers often tell themselves that it is all right to drink because "the doctor says it is". Unfor-tunately alcohol tolerance is reduced in older people. Many elderly men and women will find themselves euphoric, slightly unsteady on their feet, and a little muddled in their thinking long before they would have done when they were younger.

It is all too easy to abuse alcohol habitually. If people fall victim to the anodyne of using alcohol in the short term they may find themselves forgetful, more likely to fall, and prone to malnutrition and chronic ill health. They may not notice this them-selves and, as I have already said, their relatives and friends may only find out the cause of an elderly person's symptoms and change of character if they think of the possibility of alcohol misuse as well as looking for other likely causes for the changes that have occurred.

Cigarette-related diseases

Alcohol is a food. Cigarettes, on the other hand, are appetite suppressants. Many elderly people smoke to help them to stop overeating. They also find that cigarettes loosen sputum, benefit stool production and generally enhance their sense of well being. These short-term benefits of cigarette smoking are offset by their danger to every system in the body, especially to the heart and lungs. While it is true that some people survive into extreme old age although they drink a gallon of beer every day and smoke like a chimney, it is also true that so far no one can predict who these survivors will be. Far more people will die at a younger age than will become proud veterans if they drink and/or smoke too much. Since no one knows exactly why some people become poisoned by, or dependent on, alcohol, and others develop carcinoma of the bronchus when they smoke, even in moderation, the only safe way of helping oneself avoid the possible complications of alcohol, nicotine and tar ingestion is through total abstinence.

Drug-related diseases

People who decide not to drink alcohol or smoke cigarettes are wise. Many people, however, decide that they do not want to live those extra years that might be gained from abstinence, or they compromise and try to moderate their habits instead. Perhaps it is important to keep these issues in proportion by remembering that the substances and drugs people can buy over the counter are sometimes far less dangerous than the drugs they can obtain on prescription, such as powerful analgesics, anti-depressants and sleeping pills. There are probably many occasions on which it is more sensible to have a modest drink than to rush along to the doctor for a mood-changing pill. There may be occasions when the psychological benefits of the after-dinner cigarette, cigar or pipe, are much safer than a doctor's prescription for a tranquillizer or sleeping drug.

I have written briefly about some of the more important and common hazards to older people's health because I believe that you and I will travel more happily and healthily towards old age if we are forewarned of the various difficulties we may encounter on the way. What each of us does about it is up to the individual concerned. It seems to me, however, that we can do a great deal to help ourselves to overcome some of the obstacles that might harm our health. If we want to do that we need to arm ourselves, preferably in middle age, with courage, determination, common sense and a good sense of humour, before we set out on the next stage of the journey. Most of us will find that learning to ignore small difficulties and finding ways round the larger ones, or coming to terms with them, will stand us in good stead when we come to the life-threatening illnesses that we cannot ignore, avoid or get around.

These invasive and life-threatening illnesses are different from the hazards to health that I have been considering. They call for different strategies if we are to complete our journey with some dignity and serenity.

The End Point of Life

The End-point may be seen as the ultimate point of love; the point to which love brings all the suffering, sickness and pain: the End-point is at the gap, beyond which we cannot know.[5]

In 1977 two remarkable women came to the End-point of life. One was Mother Maria, a Swiss woman who became an Orthodox nun. She died when she was sixty-five years old, after a four-year-long battle against cancer. At the beginning of her struggles she had written:

My cancer has solved many insoluble conflicts. Anything less would not have achieved it.[6]

Two years later she was firmly in its grip, needing strong pain killers to help her to cope with the pain she was having from bone secondaries:

I am much lacking in strength and usually lie quietly, centring without words in my death-country and ever inwardly turning away from the outward things. Images, symbols, words and expressions go further and further away, and what remains is perhaps simply a total consent to that which I do not know and cannot fathom; except that I feel that sense is all around us and less and less does it matter that we should see it.[7]

Eventually the cancer spread to her brain. She suffered from double vision, giddiness, raging headaches and a series of small strokes, yet two weeks before she died she was still writing:

> So we crawl on all fours heavenwards and yet at the same time we run speedily and youthfully round all the corners without making a song about it.[8]

Mother Maria died on 25th November 1977. Less than a month later, on 20th December, another remarkable woman, Iulia de Beausobre, died at the age of eighty-four, after a long period of ill health, during which she had a slight stroke which left her unable to write. She also suffered from slurred speech and intermittent mental confusion.[9] Like Mother Maria, Iulia de Beausobre belonged to the Orthodox faith. As a young woman she had suffered greatly. Her only child had died from starvation in the first years of the Russian revolution. Her husband had been shot by the Bolsheviks, and she was imprisoned and subsequently sent to a concentration camp. On her release a year later she left Russia, came to England as a refugee and eventually made her home there.

Iulia de Beausobre's book about her experiences, *The Woman Who Could Not Die*,[10] launched her on a distinguished career as a writer. Her pamphlet on *Creative Suffering*,[11] and her account of the life of St Seraphim of Sarov, *Flame in the Snow*,[12] had a profound effect on me when I was a young woman and newly converted to Christianity. Many years later I met her when she was old, frail but still mentally alert. She was confined to one small room in an old people's home. She was well versed in suffering, "pregnant with death"[13], as she said, and she was translucent. During our meeting I saw her dying as a kind of birth into an existence beyond words or imagination, and I caught a glimpse of the reality behind those words of Mother Maria when she said that she gave "total consent to that which I do not know and cannot fathom".

Between them these two women help me to contemplate the process of dying with some equanimity. We cannot escape from that experience. We shall not know what it is like until we get there. In one sense there is no point in worrying about the future, for it will come upon us by stealth, whether we die of cancer at the age of sixty-five, or of old age at eighty-four. In another sense we need to prepare for death by looking at the worst that can happen to us with eyes of faith and hope. I remember sitting in a convent garden, talking to a nun about this. She strung all the things she dreaded together in a great list, and I could see the pain of her thoughts in her eyes — and behind the pain, the joy and assurance of abandonment to whatever lay in her own future. She said:

Physically one dreads the prospect of growing blind, tottery, mentally vulnerable, collapsed plumbing, becoming cranky, not being able to appreciate, becoming repulsive, dying in a very hygienic, but indifferent environment – if one could be assured of a Mother Teresa around. Ah! Yet, experience tells me that however ghastly things can be, at that very point He eventually returns – so into His Hands . . .[14]

As another very old nun commented, "the whole of your infirmity is part of your prayer. It takes so long . . .".[15]

Death is rather like labour before birth. Women who have been through the experience of childbirth know that as soon as they become pregnant they are subject to forces that are greater than themselves and beyond their control. From the moment of conception labour is inevitable: it may be swift and easy, long and difficult, life-giving or death-dealing, but it will happen, and there is nothing anyone can do to prevent it.

The experience of childbirth may contribute to some women's ability to act as midwives to those who are dying. I cherish a letter I received from someone who helped her husband to die. She describes his last hour:

Later on, after I was in bed, we said together the prayer we had used ever since we were first engaged, the Collect for what used to be Trinity IV beginning, "O God the protector of all that trust in Thee . . .", John made one or two drowsy comments about the family and after about a quarter of an hour at about ten to eleven

I asked him if he would like a sip of water. "A little", he said. He died as I raised his head to help him to swallow, though I didn't realize it immediately so casually had it happened.

She adds a few lines further on:

What this six months has shown us above all is that this is not an exploration to be undertaken alone. When our friends are prepared to face it with us our dying can teach us to live.[16]

I had read and re-read that letter many times before my turn came to be midwife to my own husband's dying birth. Cradled in my lap, with two of our children close by, his head turned to the fading light where he could see the trees in our garden he loved so much, longing to be born, yet unable to die, he and we lived through a long hard labour before release came. Yes, there was sorrow, but there was also joy at that moment of his birth into new life. We, who had to stay behind, were glad to have been with him when his time came.

You and I cannot postpone our appointment with birth, nor with death. We cannot foresee what will happen to us when we reach the end-points of our lives. We can however prepare. We can ask close relatives and friends to stay close to us as we make that journey. We can help them and the professionals who will care for us by telling them well ahead of time whether we want them to try to keep us alive, just for the sake of existence, if, for instance, we have a serious stroke and can only be offered a form of survival by being put on a life-support machine. After a certain age our wishes may appear to be rather academic, but we can at least make our desires known well ahead of that time. Many of us will wish to die with as much dignity and privacy as possible, and some of us may decide to refuse heroic measures which will prolong our relatives' suffering. It is up to us to retain control of ourselves for as long as we can; then, when the time comes we can trust those who care for us to do their best for us. In the end we can, I believe, trust God to see us through the experience of dying.

Finding the Victories

Introduction / Planning for the future / Seeing
through the problems / Finding the balance / Living
from conviction

Do let us see our dull, drear, ordinary pain will be
truly fringed with splendour if we learn how to make
use of it, a splendour not of this world.[1]

Introduction

Until this point in this book I have written of the
pleasures and pains of the journey from youth to age
in a descriptive way. "These are the facts: here are
some of the experiences I have had: these are some
of the people I have listened to on the way", I have
said. So far I have analysed the theme into a series of
manageable components and then worked with each
fragment of the whole. In this way I have moved
from the obvious pleasures of growing older to the
more subtle ones, from the physical problems to the
psychological and spiritual ones in that order, from
minor ailments to life-threatening illnesses. These
progressions are in tune with our journey from
middle age to very old age, for many of the real
pleasures of growing older are to be found in the

earlier phases of that journey, while many of the worst pains occur towards the end. Now I want to stand back and look at the picture as a whole rather than in an analytic way, thinking of a person's life as a portrait painted by God.

When I look at any portrait's overall composition rather than at its details I begin to see why a certain object was placed where it was in the picture, how it draws the eye to other objects which are related to it, how it contributes to the whole. I can also see that the portrait would be incomplete without each of its components being there and in the right place. When I look carefully I can see that the picture has been built up from layers of paint, that the brushwork has been skilfully applied and the highlights added to the picture as it grew as well as at the end, but I hardly notice any of that as I stand back and look at it. Sometimes when I look at the work of a greater artist I can begin to understand the mind of the painter, even though I know that my own perception colours my interpretation of what I am seeing.

I find that the analogy of God as a painter is quite helpful up to a certain point. I often feel that God paints each person's portrait as he or she grows and matures. I see God using other people and events to add a bit here, subtract a bit there, covering over some of the dark bits with highlights to distract my attention from the ugliness of some of the original mistakes. The analogy, however, cannot be pressed too far, for, even as I look, I become aware that God uses people as painters as well as inviting them to be the subjects of his painting, and that God and we are working with living materials that won't always comply with the painters' intentions. Perhaps, I think, when that happens, and we wriggle out of being either painters or subjects, God laughs a little and takes a rest, inviting us to do the same, or leaving us to struggle on by ourselves for a while.

In this section of the book I want to take a rest, stand back, see the theme as a whole, laugh a little as I see the smudges and errors and yet see beyond them to the victories that are already there, fringing "the dull, drear, ordinary pain" and events of our lives with splendour. Then when I go back to the painting of my own portrait I shall hope to see where God intends me to paint in some highlights. I know very well that you and I can only see our own lives as half-completed paintings. We cannot wholly see them as God sees them: we do not even see ourselves as others see us: we cannot yet envisage what they will look like when our lives come to their natural end. We can, however, catch a glimpse of the way things are going, and we also know that it is not too late to alter the picture quite radically by making changes in our lives which will express the mind of God and our true selves more clearly than we have so far been able to do.

Let us stand back, look at ourselves, see where we have come from and who we now are at this point in our lives. As you do this, be gentle in your appraisal of yourself. Do not tear yourself into little pieces as if you were a disposable sketch which had gone wrong.

What is your half-finished portrait telling you about your personal journey, who you have become and where you think you might be going? What do you see in the portrait of your life that might need highlighting if you are to show other people what was in the mind of God when you were created? Do any of the experiences and thoughts you and I have been sharing reverberate in your own life so that you want to alter some details in your own painting? What might you do with the rest of your life so that at its end God and you will feel pleased with the finished product?

Take time to do this, days or weeks if necessary, before you go on with your journey. I have myself done this at several points in my own life, often with the wise counsel of a trusted friend who has helped me to look at my own unfinished portrait with eyes of understanding, compassion and hope, and who has found the highlights and victories when I have seen only darkness and failure. Such reflective interludes in my life have been turning points, times when I have been able to learn lessons, find new directions, claim some victories. Having good friends to encourage, sustain and accompany me on my own journey, I have every reason to grow older with faith, hope and love as my companions. It is my hope that the same is true for many of those who read this book. If, however, it isn't, I hope you will keep on searching until you do find yourself, your soul friend and in the end, I believe, God.

When you have had a pause, a laugh, a good rest,

you will be ready for the next phase of your own journey and the next stage of this book, which offers a kind of plan that can help each of us to create the climate and circumstances that we shall need if we are to claim some victories in our lives, find the splendour that fringes pain as we grow older, and reach that point where it could be said of us that "with the ancient is wisdom and in length of days understanding".[2]

At the outset of this new journey which begins now, at this very moment, we need to realize that the spiritual growth which would allow us to become wise and understanding will take place more often in and through tiny practical everyday experiences than in and through heroic actions of our own contriving. We shall need to take account of that in making plans for the future.

Planning for the Future

Therefore do not be anxious about tomorrow, for tomorrow will be anxious for itself. Let the day's trouble be sufficient for the day.[3]

Taken literally, this familiar saying is sometimes used to justify the kind of hand-to-mouth existence that is called "faith living". According to those who think along these lines, God knows everything about us, has thought it all out ahead of time, and will supply us with all that we need, providing we are doing

God's will. All that we have to do is to ask for what we need in order to carry out God's work and, lo and behold, it will arrive. The writings of some Christians are full of stories of how someone, whose funds were about to run out, trusted in God: the next day a letter arrived with a cheque for just the right amount, no less, no more. Now I am convinced that God does bless some individuals who do his work in this way. I am sure that God places the needs of those people before others who are affluent enough, or sacrificial enough, to supply the daily needs of those who do God's work.

I am also sure, however, that it is equally God's will when things do not work out quite like that. For every story of providential help arriving in the nick of time there is a corresponding story of disappointment. It must have been someone's false optimism that provoked Benjamin Franklin into making a shrewd observation: "He that lives upon hope, will die fasting."[4] So for me there is no contradiction of principle if we take our future seriously enough to make provision for our old age, while at the same time we refuse to get worried about what might happen, or might never happen, and concentrate on getting on with today's troubles. I cannot see any virtue in refusing to make sensible plans for our old age and then appealing to the Authorized Version of the Bible to support our view.[5]

It is my belief, then, that God expects most of us to plan ahead so that we do not have to meet avoidable problems, but will be able to concentrate our energies on facing the unavoidable difficulties of each day's living. For those of us who are growing older, "Help yourself and heaven will help you",[6] is a good motto to remember whenever we notice a tendency to self-pity or false optimism creeping into our thoughts and dreams.

Before I turn to some practical ways in which we can plan for our older years, I need to grasp one nettle quite firmly. It is my belief that in the matter of old age our spiritual beliefs determine our psychological and practical attitudes towards infirmity and death.

"The only difference between you and me", said a younger friend to me recently, "is that you think there's a purpose to life and I don't. You think you're going somewhere and I don't."

I had to agree with my friend: yet I did not see what a difference it made until I came to think about death, life after death, and judgement. As a Christian I believe in resurrection, even though I acknowledge that I am content to leave to God the question of just how it happens: I do not need to penetrate that mystery in order to believe in it. I believe in judgement, though I have faith that it will be tempered by God's mercy. I am sure that these beliefs do influence my approach to the last part of my life, however short or long it is. Had I been born a Hindu and brought up to believe in reincarnation, then the tenet would have influenced my present attitudes and actions because I would believe that by working out my *karma* I would effect the way in which I would return in my next life. According to how I have lived my present life, I might be reborn to a lower or higher state: under certain circumstances I might be absorbed into God and not have to return to earth at all. Were I to be a Muslim I should be upset if by now I had not made at least one pilgrimage to Mecca: I might welcome a martyr's death as a guarantee of a safe passage to heaven. So I agree with my friend that our religious attitudes towards death and judgement influence our attitudes towards the way we live our lives. Yet, at the same time, I am not nearly so sure that faith affects our attitude towards the act of dying itself.

I may, and probably will, spend the last years of my own life trying to draw closer to God in whom we "live and move and have our being".[7] I imagine that my atheist friends will spend their last years in different ways. Yet all of us will hope that during the later years of our time we will be able to get a good deal of enjoyment out of life, and that when we come to the last months, days, hours or moments of life we will be cared for with compassion and enabled to die with dignity. Dying will test our faith: yet because we are human those of us who have religious faith and those of us who do not will share many hopes and experiences as we approach our own dying.

Having grasped the nettle of the question of how religious belief may alter how we think of and what we do about old age, dying and death, I want to allow faith, or its absence, to undergird some of our responses to some very practical questions of how you and I are going to make plans for the way we want to spend our old age, assuming that we will live that long.

I realize that some people will decline to make any provision for old age at all, but many of us do think long and hard about it as we approach retirement, and then again as we realize that we are becoming old or ill, so old or ill that it is getting hard to continue as before. If then you, like me, do want to think ahead, first to retirement, then to what to do in making provision for real old age or infirmity, you may like to ask yourselves the kind of questions I have been glad to ask myself already, and intend to go on asking at regular intervals for the rest of my life.

1. Are you still able to live independently?

2. If so, and you decide to live on your own or with an ageing spouse or friend, what can you do now to make your home safe, warm and enjoyable for the future?

3. If you live independently what have you done to make things easier for other people, in the event of your being taken ill, or dying suddenly?

   a) Are your doctor's /vicar's telephone numbers visible near your own phone?

b) Does a friendly neighbour have a key to your home so that she/he can get in easily if you have an accident, or are suddenly taken ill?

c) Do you have a list of telephone numbers handy so that important people in your life can be notified of your illness or death?

d) Have you got a spare set of night clothes, toilet articles and other important things ready, in case you need to be taken to hospital in the middle of the night?

e) Have you made a will? If so, will anyone be able to find it?

f) Are all your legal and financial papers in order?

g) Do your close relatives know what your wishes are as regards your resuscitation, funeral, or disposition of effects not covered by your will?

4. Can you imagine living with any of your relatives or friends?

5. If so, when will be the best time to move?

6. If, not, what are you going to do when you become too old for independent living?

7. Have you yet reached the point when you think that you ought to get your name on a

waiting list for sheltered housing or an old people's home?

8. What would you like to do before you die?

   a) Is there anything you need to put right, or want to?

   b) Is there anyone you need to forgive? Or be forgiven by?

   c) Is there anything you really want to do that you have not done before? If so do it now, or as soon as possible.

9. What is the worst thing that you can imagine happening to you? And the best?

10. What do you personally believe about life after death?

When you have answered these questions you may be surprised by some of the facts they reveal about yourself. These surprises may be quite pleasant. I was certainly pleased to find that one result of recently asking them of myself was that I was able to make some sensible changes to the way I needed to reorganize my home life in order to help me look after my husband as he became more frail. We made these changes together, and planned them with an eye to my future life when I would be on my own. I have, for instance, spent some of my present relatively high income on durable goods, which will help me to remain independent for as long as possible. The central heating is now gas-fired and my old coal scuttles have disappeared. An automatic washing machine has replaced a twin-tub. A small rotovator and easy-to-manage, self-propelled mowing machine have added to the joys of gardening. The kitchen has been rearranged to make it easier to manage. Of course, we had to make some sacrifices in order for me to have these material possessions: holidays, new clothes, meals out took a back seat for quite a while.

I regard all these changes as a sign of victory over a certain puritanical temperament which regards all luxury as self-indulgent, a disposition in me that was reinforced by economic necessity during the years when our children were growing up. When they were grown up I was not at all sure that I could learn to spend money on myself, and it was a real struggle to change the habits of a lifetime. The victory feels good!

Other people might make quite different choices about their pre-retirement spending. You might choose a cruise, hi-fi equipment, or a new car. You might not be affluent enough to make those sorts of choices at all: for you it might mean rearranging the kitchen cupboard, and throwing away some things you never use so that you can put what is left in places which you can reach more easily. However rich or poor you are you do have some choices to make, and they will probably have more spiritual import than you might think.

Although I have just described some changes that

have happened to me in a rather prosaic way, I know deep down inside myself that they represent an important shift in my life from one phase to another. I have started to think of myself as a recipient of a pension, one who will expect to remain independent for as long as possible, but who will eventually have to learn how to come to the fourth phase of life, the phase of contemplation, of pensivity, of dependence on others, of waiting for death – not gloomily but expectantly, even hopefully, for as the strength of the body declines, so, I believe, the spirit will grow until it is born anew, reclothed in eternity.

An enclosed nun drew my attention to this positive way of looking at declining physical strength and increasing spiritual growth when we were talking about a title for this book. She said that "we must stress the 'growing' old, not just the 'getting' old. 'Growing' denotes something positive and up-building, whereas 'getting' old might suggest a form of decline or decay."[8] I have sometimes had to hang on to the memory of our talk together, because it is not at all easy to see old age, and the suffering that it often entails, in a positive way, when all that seems to lie ahead is a kind of waiting for death.

W. H. Vanstone has written helpfully on this phase of life in his book *The Stature of Waiting*, where he refers to the holiness of waiting which

> can be the most intense and poignant of all human experiences – the experience which, above all others, strips us of affectation and self-

deception and reveals to us the reality of our needs, our values and ourselves.[9]

Vanstone associates this kind of waiting, which is especially linked with inescapable suffering, with Christ's waiting in the Garden of Gethsemane, when he contemplated the possibility of the suffering that might lie ahead of him and yet totally surrendered himself to God's will, so that he could accept relief at God's hand or endure the Cross. That waiting figure of Christ tells us about how God looks at waiting, passivity and dependence. It also offers us a way of acceptance which enables us to contemplate our own waiting as a way of walking in Christ's footsteps, a way of passivity which is also a way of active acceptance, even though we know that our sufferings are trivial compared with his. Vanstone sees dignity in this kind of waiting, a dignity which is invested in humankind by God, in whose image men and women are created:

Man must see his dignity not only in being a point of activity in the world, but also a point of receptivity: not only in the manifold capacity for action but also in the many facets of his passivity; not only in his potential for "doing" but also in his exposure to "being done to". He must not see it as degrading that he should wait upon the world, be helped, be provided for, be dependent; for as such he is by God's gift, what God himself makes himself to be.[10]

The contemplation of these great truths about the fourth "waiting" phase of our lives is not confined to Christians. I have written from within the Christian tradition because it is the one I am steeped in, and because my faith is an integral part of myself. In writing in this way I am not trying to impose my own beliefs on other people, but I am trying to suggest that all of us, whatever our beliefs, can look beyond the practical plans that we sensibly make to their implications and to their ultimate meaning in our lives.

You and I are on a journey towards death. On that journey we shall meet some problems. We may meet them head-on. We may ignore them. We may get round them. It may help us to cope with them if we see through them.

Seeing through the Problems

The deformities and ugly changes likely to be brought by decline must be seen through rather than ignored in order to reach and acknowledge the particular beauty, truth and goodness of spirit which can dwell within.[11]

When I was a young doctor I tended to ignore deformity and ugly changes. I would find myself pretending that someone was not an alcoholic but only a heavy drinker, or that another client was not dying, when she was. I would often shut my eyes to the ugly truths about the deteriorating relationships between husband and wife, in the hope that their problem would eventually evaporate. I certainly ignored some of my own defects and thought of myself as a professional carer rather than as a human being who was a medical practitioner.

Later, when I trained in psychiatry, I learnt to recognize the various deformities and ugly changes that occur in life, so I stopped trying to ignore them. That brought its own difficulties because solving the problems became the major occupation of my professional life.

I was well on into the middle years of life, with some psychiatric and theological training behind me, before I began to see through the problems. It was only then that I began to realize that I was not going to overcome all the various problems that were interfering with my own and other people's enjoyment of life. It was then that I found that I could go beyond the immediate relationship, or activity, to the reality that lay within and beyond it.

As I have grown older I have increasingly sought to allow the reality within myself to meet the reality that is in others. It has been through these sorts of wordless, even feelingless, encounters that the centre of my being has been nourished, comforted and strengthened, in and through the sharing and bearing of the pains and problems of life. I had seen that kind of meeting many times before between the very young, who are innocent, and the very old, who are transparent, but I now know that it is possible between people of any age, provided that they are willing to look for that "particular beauty, truth and goodness of spirit which can dwell within", that Sybil Harton speaks about in the passage quoted from at the beginning of this section.

It is difficult to explain this kind of "seeing through" in words, but one writer, Iulia de Beausobre, lifts the veil on such "seeing" in her book about St Serafim of Sarov, who lived from 1759 to 1883. Serafim was a monk, a hermit for part of his life, a living icon of God for hundreds of people who came to his monastery to be touched by his holiness. His biographer tells of an incident which happened towards the end of his life. Serafim is in the kitchen garden, felling logs. A layman called Nicholas joins him. They talk. The younger man speaks of his longing to see God.

> Putting down his axe Serafim came forward. Nicholas rose. The cripple gripped him by the shoulders and said, "We're both in the spirit now. Look at me."
>
> "I can't. It hurts my eyes."
>
> "Fear nothing. Look."
>
> In the centre of a huge radiant sun, the well known, well loved face smiled. Nicholas saw the speaking lips move, the expression in the deep blue eyes change. He heard the voice, felt the grip of hands. But those hands as well as Nicholas' own shoulders and Serafim's body, were lost in a brightness that obliterated them and inun-

dated the whole clearing, burnishing the flakes
of falling snow and the snow on the ground to a
shining whiteness . . .

Reflecting the light, Serafim's eyes sparkled.
"The grace of God is in you and you are in it. If
you could only see how your face shines. Will
you always remember the grace that has been
lavished on you, my joy?"

"And me not even a monk!"

"That's nothing. It is to man, not to his state
or condition, that God says 'Child, give me your
heart'. If we give it, he comes."[12]

When I first read the description I was much younger
than I now am. It was the words of Nicholas, "And
me not even a monk", and Serafim's reply, that stuck
in my mind and encouraged me to seek similar
encounters with God in and through other people. I
needed to see the glory of God. I have seen it, at first
in monks and nuns, then in many quite ordinary
men, women and children with whom I have had the
privilege of spending time.

These encounters have been precious. I seek them
because I know they will help me to expose the ugly
problems and distortions of life, whilst still seeing
them in the context of ultimate reality. I seek them
because I know that there is no way of overcoming
the problems of ageing from outside, yet see that they
can be dissolved by the light that is within, the light
that transfigures our meanness and helps us to catch
glimpses of the reality that is God. As I grow older

my attention is focused increasingly to the heavenly, secret significance of other people's lives.[13]

Whatever you and I may have done in the past, whoever we have been, we will do well, I believe, to spend a considerable part of our years of declining strength in the contemplation of the reality that lies within and beyond our problems. That reality is to be found in the depths of our being, where, so I believe, dwells the Spirit who will bring us safely through the labour of dying to that end which is also a beginning, to that condition about which T. S. Eliot speaks in the last lines of his poem, *East Coker*:

> Old men ought to be explorers,
> Here and there does not matter.
> We must be still and still moving
> Into another intensity
> For a further union, a deeper communion
> Through the dark cold and
>   the empty desolation,
> The wave cry, the wind cry,
>   the vast waters
> Of the petrel and the porpoise.
>   in my end is my beginning.[14]

There is no way of teaching ourselves to be explorers. We just have to begin. We are never going to be too old to begin. I think I began a long time ago; yet, as I grow older I still find myself eager to set out anew. Past experience has helped me to uncover some helpful ways of preparing for this kind of exploration:

1. Cultivate the habit of silence for a few minutes each day.

2. Listen to the tiny noises that you hear in the silence.

3. Listen to the meaning of what you hear.

4. Rediscover wonder.

5. When you go to meet another person wipe your mind clean of its preconceptions about that person.

6. Take some silence into your meeting with him or her, indeed with everyone.

7. Learn to look beyond what you see at once, to that which is hidden and precious.

8. Take time to listen to what the very old and the very young have to say, even if at first it sounds like rubbish.

9. Be especially attentive to anything which seems to contradict your own opinion, or stretches your mind to take in an entirely new thought.

10. Put yourself in the way of meeting those who live from conviction, even if you are not convinced by the faith which sustains them.

I should like to say that I make these suggestions as much to myself and to fellow Christians as to other people who do not share our religious faith. We Christians can be so busy thinking good thoughts, quoting from the Bible and praying to God in words of our own making that we forget God's command to "be still and know that I am God".[15] If we become too busy talking to God and doing all kinds of good works we may find ourselves trying to dowse the flames of some burning bush we find in our path, as Moses did. We may never stop to ask ourselves important questions, as he did, or hear God speak to us out of the burning bush, as he did.[16] Worse still, on other occasions — when we do not hear the voice of God even in the fire, or, perhaps, like Elijah, are cast down and in hiding, and see that the fire consumes all that it touches — we may not stay around for long enough to hear that "still small voice" of God that Elijah heard, after the wind and the earthquake and the fire had raged over Mount Horeb.[17] If we really want to hear that "still small voice" and are prepared to look, listen, and wait, we shall hear it, sometimes where we expect to hear it, sometimes in wholly unexpected places, people and circumstances.

If we choose to use some precious time to contemplate God, and many older people do so choose, we shall need to find a balance between activity and passivity, doing and being, giving and receiving. The search for balance is part of our exploration. It is also part of our maturing.

Finding the Balance

The key to a successful older life is the wisdom that comes from the way of integration.[18]

Once people have made sensible plans for their future, and have found a way of seeing through their problems, they are ready to harmonize the positive and negative elements in their lives, external and internal, so as to find a balance between them.

Many people never do this work, either because they die before they have had a chance to reach maturity or because they do not see the importance of integration and its relation to the whole of their lives.

I must admit that the idea of becoming a "balanced person" sounds rather dull and not at all adventurous. I know that when I was young I was quite glad to be thought an "unbalanced" young woman, because I can remember looking askance at the rather dull, mousey, even-tempered, middle-aged, nicely mannered, respectable professional women, whom I associated with the concept of a "balanced personality" at that time of my life.

"I'm not going to become like them," I told myself,

as I set off to pursue my own medical career in a highly individual, slightly eccentric way.

Now that I'm older, and, hopefully, a little wiser, I realize that I had an erroneous notion of what balance means. When I was a young woman I saw balance as monotonous, static, boring. Now I see that what matters is not so much the evenness of opposing qualities within a person's life experience or personality, as the tension that exists between those opposing elements. That tension is what makes, or can make, our lives polychromatic, dynamic and exciting, however long or short they are.

External tensions in our lives will always occur. We may have great, or little, control over them; they may be comfortable, or distressing, according to circumstances. We can suffer great stress as we experience the strain of these various tensions. Sometimes we will find the stress too much, and become quite ill because of it. At other times, when the stress is not too great, we may be able to use tension creatively, acquire experience of handling it efficiently, and grow through it. External tensions, however, are unlikely to affect us unless they disturb the internal balance of the different and opposing elements within our own personalities. These internal tensions are very important; they often command our attention, even when we would rather disregard them.

The struggle between warring elements in people's personalities causes a kind of see-saw, or, alternatively, a kind of internal tug-of-war that sets up a feeling of tension within. The stronger the pull is in one direction, the stronger the pull needs to be in the other if one element is to prevent the other from dominating the contest. The fact that the opposing elements within many people's characters are often unevenly matched means that some parts of their personalities which are weak have to be complemented and supported by other qualities. Thus it often happens that talents which once lay dormant begin to develop in order to reinforce the weakest part of someone's identity, so preventing the stronger element from dominating and unbalancing that person's entire life.

This kind of internal struggle can be very productive, so that by the time one is middle aged, or approaching retirement, the balancing work has been done. In that case, one has become quite a pleasant person to live with, simply because the self-understanding required for such a balance has led to more self-acceptance and increased ability to tolerate moderate tension in one's life. Unfortunately, however, this does not always happen. The internal struggle may grow wearisome, especially as people grow older, when they sometimes become less inhibited by convention. Moreover, some people are not aware that there is any struggle at all: they simply expect other people to tolerate the ill-temper and quirkiness that spills over from their internal tensions. As they grow older life becomes increasingly unpleasant for themselves and for others alike.

It is not at all unusual for women and men to

experience this kind of disturbing, anxiety-provoking tension as they get older, have less external distractions to preoccupy them, and more time to spend on their relationships with partners and friends. Sometimes close relatives find themselves on the receiving end of these tensions. I have met many relatives who are bewildered and distressed by the changes that have come over an ageing spouse or parent. Sometimes the changes are so great that they amount to a complete change of personality.

I remember one old man to whom this kind of sad change happened. He had always been a kind, gentle man. In his old age he remained just such a person to everyone outside his immediate family, but he became critical of his wife and children, verbally aggressive towards his children, and physically aggressive towards his wife whenever they were alone. The problem came to light when he attacked her by hitting her over the head with a handy table lamp. During a long period of counselling it turned out that he had buried a resentment about something his wife had done many years before. He had never spoken openly about it, and indeed had forgotten the incident entirely until it was recovered during the counselling. He had stifled the resentment but it had caused internal tension: eventually the tension had become too much for him. He had allowed his resentment to get the upper hand so that it spilled over into physical violence.

Happily for that old man, his wife and family, that

incident provided the help they needed. Balance and harmony were restored; reconciliation came about both within his personality and within the family. But some people are not so fortunate.

If this kind of experience is not to happen to us when we get older, you and I may need to look at the tensions within our own lives and personalities now, while we are still young enough to bring about the necessary changes that will enable us to use those tensions creatively, instead of allowing them to dominate our entire lives. One good way of looking at the various tensions that may be present in us is to ask ourselves some very practical questions:

1. What do you most like about yourself?

2. What do you least like?

3. Is there a relation between these qualities?

4. Which has the upper hand?

5. Do you ever see those qualities in others who live close to you? Do you relate to them in an emotive way? If so, what does that tell you about yourself?

6. Who could you talk to about your unfulfilled hopes?

7. How could you share something you find difficult to talk about with someone you trust? Are there better ways than speech?

8. How do you help other people to talk to you? If they don't, why not?

9. How can you change what can be changed, and accept what cannot be changed? Can you tell the difference?

10. How will people remember you when you are dead?

I do not think we should be afraid of trying to understand ourselves. I know that our perception of the truth will be incomplete and that we cannot know ourselves as God knows us, but I do think there is value in periodic reviews of our own assets and liabilities. This should never be a navel-gazing exercise but a discipline undertaken in order to help us find balance, the kind of balance that gives harmony to our own lives and happiness to other people.

Questionnaires, such as the one I have outlined, offer one kind of opportunity to make an assessment. Another task we can set ourselves is that of writing one's own obituary. Another gentler way, though just as effective, is to write one's own life story, not necessarily for publication to the world, but certainly for oneself and one's immediate family.

If you find it difficult to recover long-lost memories

in one of the ways suggested, you may find it more helpful to reflect on a shorter period of time, such as the past years, or even a few months, if they have been eventful. You may like to do this by going away to a monastic house or retreat centre, where you can be quiet and on your own, though not alone. The rhythms of regular worship, structured silence, and God-centred commitment, is conducive to meditative thought and prayer. Most people, but by no means all, who go to stay at a monastery or convent for a few days are themselves practising Christians. Everyone is welcome. Monastic hospitality is simple and generous. Monks and nuns do not intrude on people's privacy, but in my experience they always make themselves available to guests who want to talk to them. These days many monks and nuns are elderly themselves, and they understand older people's problems very well, though as one active old nun wrote to me recently, "As you can imagine, convent life doesn't allow much time to think about ageing. One just does it!" Watching the nuns "just doing it" in the religious community to which I belong as a kind of "hanger on", I find my visits restful and refreshing. Whenever I go to the convent I can recover my balance and find the harmonies again, as the discordant elements in my own personality become more integrated. When it is time to go home I usually find that I am refreshed and strengthened for the living that lies ahead.

If you try any of these exercises I think you will be pleasantly surprised by some of the discoveries you will make. Looking back can become a way of helping yourself to look forward. It can become a way of looking beyond the details of events and relationships to the wellsprings of one's being, to one's hopes and disappointments, successes and failures, short- and long-term relationships. You will probably come to see how past events and relationships have contributed to the formation of your personality as you know it today. You may even find yourself wanting to make some alteration to the way you behave and live. These changes may affect your future. They may even affect your dying.

Living from Conviction

At any moment now Death may say to me
"It is time now for us to become one!"[19]

The closer we get to death the more urgent it becomes to live each day as if it were one's last, not morbidly, but thankfully and joyfully, looking steadily at death's approach.

Death is a friend to us all in the end. We need to get ready to welcome "our sister the death body" (as St Francis of Assisi called that friend) a long way ahead of the moment of our dying.[20] It will be in that relationship with our own mortality that we will learn how to live from conviction.

We shall all die. That fact is an inescapable part of our living. Victory comes when we learn how to live with the inevitability of our own death with conviction, the kind of conviction that John Donne speaks of in one of his poems:

> Since I am coming to that Holy Room
> Where, with thy choir of Saints,
>   for evermore
> I shall be made Thy music, as I come
> I tune my instrument here at the door
> And what I must do then, think here
>   before.[21]

I know that for many people alive today there is no Holy Room, no choir of Saints, no music, only the door. These people will not be able to think about eternity in the same way that John Donne did, and others of us still do. Nevertheless, even if the concepts of resurrection life and eternal life are meaningless to some readers, I have reached the point in the book where I must declare my own convictions about death, for it is those deeply held beliefs which give purpose to my life.

I often wish that the Christian Church would take a leaf out of the Hindu religion and devise a rite for abandoning the world in old age, similar to, but not the same as, the one available to Hindus.[22] A devout Hindu can prepare for death by becoming a *sanyasi*, an ascetic who has renounced the world, abandoned his home and all who are precious to him. On the day that he enters this state the candidate, who has prepared for this moment by fasting and prayer, takes a pot of water in his hand and pours the water on the ground. By this symbolic activity he should announce that from now on he has left all worldly connections and all desires of the flesh . . . Later he plunges into the river, unties all his clothes and lets them float away in the stream. The Act of Incorporation follows as his teacher or guide conducts him out of the water, and gives him a loin cloth, an upper garment and a staff. He is now *sanyasi* or an ascetic who has renounced the world.[23]

Between that moment and his death the *sanyasi* will "wander ceaselessly from place to place, in silence and solitude, stripped of everything",[24] dependent for life itself on the alms of others.

According to tradition, *Sanyasa* should only be taken late in life when a person has fulfilled all the duties of adult life and has heirs to care for those who are left behind. This state of life is not to be equated with the "fourth state of life" which follows the three previous stages of being a student, a householder and retirement. According to Abishikitinanda, a Christian monk who knew the Hindu tradition very well, *Sanyasa*:

belongs to no category whatever and cannot be undertaken along with anything else. It is truly transcendent, as God himself transcends all, being apart from all, beyond all, yet immanent in all without any duality.[25]

When the *sanyasi* puts on the flame-coloured robe which is the mark of his calling he will become for others:

> a sign of the divine Presence, a witness to the mystery which is beyond all signs, a reminder to every man of the mystery of his own true self.[26]

Western Christianity has no rite of passage to set alongside this Hindu one, but some Christians – such as the French Benedictine monk, Henri le Saux, who took the name of Abishikitinanda – have likened this embracing of *Sanyasa* to the call to solitude which attracted so many men and women to the Egyptian desert in the third and fourth centuries of Christianity. The same call to solitary contemplation happens to some people today.

I am not suggesting that it should be everyone's duty to abandon everything to become a *sanyasi*. That vocation is only for those called to it. I do think, however, that we can learn from that tradition: there are some elements in it that remind me of the great Christian tradition of renunciation of everything for the love of God.[27] Some people embrace this ascetic way of life literally. Others understand it as an underlying principle of the Christian way, a way of setting one's face towards heaven that helps one to long to reach the further shore. All of us, I believe, are indebted to monks and nuns who witness to the primacy of their faith by their willingness to live a life of prayer and self-sacrifice. Their witness helps us to live and die in the convictions of our faith.

It seems to me that there is a point at which all of us turn away from life as we have known it, towards the life we cannot know about before we die. We cannot anticipate that moment but we can approach it with awe and without repugnance, in the kind of way I find expressed in two contemporary pieces of writing. The first is a poem called *After Ninety*:

Any time now
I shall look up from reading
And wonder for a moment
Who it is
Seated there
In the Queen Anne chair
With unfathomable eyes
Waiting for me to recognize
The finality of his regard.

It may be in the morning
As I lie in the bath
The hoover droning in the hall.
He will appear in the steam
Above the taps
Amused perhaps
At my immersion
As before my first incursion
Into an unknown world.

Will he alight on the table
At tea time
And call my name

In a voice like trumpets
Absolute among the crumpets?
Or shall I sense his presence still
And sombre on the window sill
Obscuring the houses opposite?

Any time now
In the long slow-turning hours
After midnight
He will be standing by my bed,
Silently I shall be led
Through the house to that hidden door
Never seen before
Though it has been there always.[28]

In this poem the writer juxtaposes the everyday
events of a woman's life with the quixotic intrusion
of death. She captures the immediacy of death that is
ever present to the very old who await their end. She
does not attempt to look beyond the moment of
death, but points to our helplessness in the face of
our own mortality.

The second piece of writing comes from the spiritual journal of my husband. It was written in his
eighty-sixth year of life, at a time when he knew that
death was imminent:

I walk hand in hand with Death;
my one companion is my faith
that the energy called life
is a gift of love from God,
given to me in the ecstasy of love

by my father and mother
some eighty-six years ago

This energy is now me, together
with the atoms of my body
which are now absorbed and excreted,
but which were created by the love
of God at the beginning of time.

Any moment now Death may say to me
"It is time now for us to become one."

What then will that next moment be?
as death takes over that energy of life?
Will my body no longer be able to
experience anything?

Faith tells us that I will
experience the beauty of God.
Faith tells me that if God loves me
He will keep me in existence
as part of His creative will.[29]

I remember discussing this meditation on death with Leo. He understood the immediacy of death, even while he clung to and enjoyed life to the full. He felt helpless and he knew the darkness of doubt, despite a lifetime spent as a Christian priest. He sought in this meditation to respond to what he felt was going to be a dissipation of energy and a scattering of atoms with an act of faith that God would in some mysterious way preserve the entity of those atoms, albeit in a different way from anything he had hitherto experienced. His response of faith was an act of conviction in the face of the unknown. Over a period of years I had watched many such acts of conviction become a way of living by faith, if faith be defined as "the assurance of things hoped for, the conviction of things not seen".[30]

My husband lived by conviction. To the end of his life he held on to that quotation which comes from the author of the Letter to the Hebrews in the New Testament. The Letter to the Hebrews has strengthened the faith of many Christians, and one of them, Bishop George Appleton, testifies to his experience that faith:

> consists of following knowledge and reason as far as they will take us, and then going beyond in the same direction. There is a risk about faith, which can only be tested by taking the leap when the sure path comes to an end.[31]

Faith is a risk; it is a leap into the unknown; it is an act of conviction. Yet, in my husband, and in some other very old people I have known, I have seen a serenity in the face of doubt that speaks to me of their profound faith. Their confidence helps me to understand the great trust which Christ showed on the Cross, when in an act of total self-surrender he spoke those last words of triumphant conviction as he died, "It is finished",[32] and "Father, into thy hands I commit my spirit".[33]

Ever since I was a small girl I have lived with people much older than I was. As I have grown older myself I have watched my husband's struggles to live a faith-centred life. I have profited from the thoughts and prayers of many enclosed nuns and monks with whom I have been closely associated. I have learnt how to die by watching other people die. I have been greatly influenced by the patient hope of very old people, who know that each moment of each day may be their last on earth, and who are nevertheless determined to enjoy and make the fullest possible use of that moment. I find in such people a kind of abandonment to divine providence, and a willingness to live or die according to God's will that teaches me more about God than anything else I can think of.

St Paul sets this abandonment to God in the context of faith in a letter he wrote from prison, when he was under the sentence of death. It was written to Christians in Rome:

> None of us lives to himself, and none of us dies to himself. If we live, we live to the Lord, and if we die, we die to the Lord; so, then, whether we live or whether we die, we are the Lord's. For to this end Christ died and lived again, that he might be the Lord both of the dead and of the living.[34]

During the writing of this book there have been many occasions when I have had to ask myself what I mean when I use words like "faith", "conviction" and "commitment". I have found it impossible to give precise definitions that would satisfy everyone. Moreover, I have found it quite difficult to explain what I mean when I say that I try to live "by faith", or "by conviction", or say that I am a "committed Christian". Oh, yes, I know the theory, but I find it difficult to work out how the theory translates into practice in my own life. So I have tended to approach issues to do with faith, conviction and commitment in a slightly oblique way: I would like to invite you to share in some of the questions I have been asking myself. Again, you will find that some of them are so simple and practical that they can be answered in a word or two; but if you then look at how you have answered you may see beyond your response to what prompted you to answer in that particular way:

1. Does your life have a purpose?

2. If so, how would you explain it to someone else?

3. If not, what gives it its zest?

4. What do you think is going to happen to you when you die?

5. Does that belief make any difference at all to the way you now live your life?

6. Whose death has influenced your own beliefs about life after death most? Least? Why?

7. What quotations (from the Bible or anywhere else) come into your mind when you hear words like the following?

   faith

   commitment

   death

   eternal life

8. When you know that your turn has come to die, to whom do you think you might turn to talk about it? Who do you think could give you the most help? And why?

9. Have you yet told anyone what you want to happen to you when you are dying? Do you, for example, want anyone to read prayers or extracts from the Bible to you? Will you want to see a priest, or be anointed?

10. What kind of a funeral do you want?

Facing up to the reality of death is an important task, and it is one that we do well to think about ahead of time. It is surprising to me how few people do either ask or attempt to answer the kind of questions I have been putting to myself for some time.

If you happen to die in hospital or a nursing home, and you are a Roman Catholic, you will probably find that a priest is automatically sent for if you are in any danger of death. Otherwise you will probably have to make your own arrangments. It is not always easy to do that. In the event of your having a stroke and being unable to speak, or being unconscious, it may be impossible to communicate your wishes to anyone. So it is as well either to make your wishes known to a close relative or trusted friend, or to write them down somewhere where they can get seen in the event of a serious illness. If you are indifferent as to what happens or does not happen to you, obviously such arrangements are unnecessary, but even then you may avoid confusion among your relatives and professional carers if you actually state this.

In my work as a deaconess of the Church of England I have usually found it wise to talk to people about their dying well ahead of time. I have found that I have often been the only person to know exactly what someone wants to happen to them when they are dying, or how they want to see their funeral conducted. There are exceptions, of course, but the difficulties I have described are very common. I know why this is, for I myself found it very difficult to talk with my husband about his wishes in these matters, so I know how painful it can be. That is why it is often easier to talk to a professional carer like a doctor, solicitor, pastor or priest.

One of my elderly nun friends recently said to me: "I was fourteen when the phrase in *The Imitation of Christ* hit me: 'Happy is the man who has the hour of death before his eyes, and daily prepareth himself to die."[35] She seems to have spent a large part of her rich life preparing for death. She is serenely happy because she is still strong enough to attend all the worship services in chapel and do her full share of each day's work in the convent where she lives.[36]

I look at my nun friend's zest for life, and I pray to God that I will be given the strength and courage to grow older as she and so many of my other friends have done. Yet even if I am not given the time or circumstances of an active old age and gentle death, I know that at this moment I desire to trust in God. It is God who will lead me through the valley of the shadow of death and bring me safely into the house of the Lord where I will dwell for ever.[37] God will, I believe, take that desire, however faint it is, and enable it to grow into conviction. God will do this, not only for me but for all who are humble enough to receive the gift of faith, even at the moment of death.

I cannot do better than to conclude this book on growing older with some words from St Paul which have come to me so many times that they have written themselves into the very fabric of my life, and sustain me as I grow older and approach the mystery of death:

We know that in everything God works for good with those who love him, who are called according to his purpose. For those whom he foreknew he also predestined to be conformed to the image of his Son, in order that he might be the first-born among many brethren. And those whom he predestined he also called: and those whom he called he also justified; and those whom he justified he also glorified.

What then shall we say to this? If God is for us, who is against us? He who did not spare his own Son but gave him up for us all, will he not also give us all things with him? Who shall bring any charge against God's elect? It is God who justifies; who is to condemn? Is it Christ Jesus, who died, yes, who was raised from the dead, who is at the right hand of God, who indeed intercedes for us? Who shall separate us from the love of Christ? Shall tribulation, or distress, or persecution, or famine, or nakedness, or peril, or sword? As it is written,

> "For thy sake we are being killed all the
>   day long
> we are regarded as sheep to be
>   slaughtered."

No, in all these things we are more than conquerers through him who loved us. For I am sure that neither death, nor life, nor angels, nor principalities, nor things present, nor things to come, nor powers, nor height, nor depth, nor anything else in all creation, will be able to separate us from the love of God in Christ Jesus our Lord.[38]

REFERENCES

Introduction

1. Collins, Mortimer, *The Unknown Quality*. Quoted in the *Oxford Dictionary of Quotations (O.D.Q.)*, O.U.P., 1953, p. 153. No 19.
2. Steele, Sir Richard, *The Spectator*, No 268. Quoted in O.D.Q., O.U.P., 1953, p. 511, No 21.
3. Stevenson, R.L., *Crabbed Age and Youth*. Quoted in O.D.Q., O.U.P., 1953, p. 514, No. 37.
4. ibid., p. 514. No 34
5. Camus, A., *A Treasury of Quotations on Christian Themes*, ed. C. E. Simcox, S.P.C.K., 1976, p. 66. No 713.
6. Shakespeare, W., *As You Like It*, Act 2, Scene 7, line 157.
7. ibid., lines 165–6.

Chapter 1. The Pleasures of Growing Older

1. Harton, Sybil, *On Growing Old*, Hodder & Stoughton, 1957, p.7.
2. Anon: Found in Rochester Cathedral c. 1970. The full quotation continues:

   Teach me the glorious lesson that occasionally it is possible that I may be mistaken. Make me thoughtful but not moody; helpful, but not bossy; Thou knowest, Lord, that what I want is a few friends at the end.

3. Eliot, T. S., "The Love Song of J. Alfred Prufrock". *Complete Poems and Plays*, Faber & Faber Ltd., 1969, p. 16.
4. Joseph, Jenny, "Warning", *The Faber Book of 20th*

Century Women's Poems and Plays, Faber & Faber Ltd., 1987, p. 229.

5. Browning, R., "Rabbi Ben Ezra"., *The Poetical Works of Robert Browning, Vol. 1.*, Smith, Elder & Co., 1899, p. 580.

6. Carroll, Lewis, *Alice's Adventures in Wonderland with Bruno's Revenge*, T. Nelson & Co., 1925, Chapter 5, p. 126.

7. Basset, Bernard, S. J., *The Noon Day Devil*, Burns & Oates, 1964, p. 112.

8. Schopenhauer, A., Quoted in *A Treasury of Quotations on Christian Themes*, ed. C. E. Simcox, S.P.C.K., 1976, p. 67, No 722.

9. Shakespeare, W., *Henry V* Act 4, Scene 3, lines 24–35.

10. Stevenson, R. L., *Crabbed Age and Youth*. Quoted in O.D.Q., O.U.P., 1953, p. 514, No 38. The full text is as follows:

    To love playthings well as a child, to lead an adventurous and honourable youth, and to settle when the time arrives into a green and smiling age, is to be a good artist in life and deserve well of yourself and your neighbour.

11. Waller, E., *The Works of the English Poets from Chaucer to Cowper*, S. Johnson, 1810, Vol. 8, p. 81 Quoted by W. Syles in *Visions of Faith*, Eden Press, 1986, p. 9.

12. Hazlitt, William., Quoted in *A Treasury of Quotations on Christian Themes*, C. E. Simcox, S.P.C.K., 1976, p. 230, No 2786.

13. Blake, W., Quoted in *Testament of Immortality*, ed. N. G., Faber & Faber, 1940, p. 107

14. Küng, Hans, *Eternal Life*, Collins, 1984.

15. St Paul's Letter to Corinthians, 15;42–44 (A.V.):

    So also is the resurrection of the dead. It is sown in corruption; it is raised in incorruption:

    It is sown in dishonour; it is raised in glory: it is sown in weakness; it is raised in power:

> It is sown a natural body; it is raised a spiritual body. There is a natural body, and there is a spiritual body.

16. Tolstoy Leo, *War and Peace*. Quoted in *Testament of Immortality*, ed. N. G., Faber & Faber, 1940, p. 169.
17. de Chardin, Teilhard, *Le Milieu Divin*, Collins, 1960, p. 61.
18. Fox, George, quoted in *Testament of Immortality*, ed. N. G., Faber & Faber, 1940, p. 230.
19. q.v. Holy Bible, Revised Standard Version (R.S.V.): Psalms 23 and 121; John 14: 1–3; 1 Corinthians 15; 1 Thessalonians 4:13–18; Revelation 21:1–7.
20. Job 12:2 (R.S.V.).

Chapter 2. The Problems of Growing Older

1. Franklin, B., quoted in *A Treasury of Quotations on Christian Themes*, ed. C. E. Simcox, S.P.C.K., 1976, p. 67, No 721.
2. Appleton, George, *Journey for a Soul*, Collins, 1976, p. 47.
3. de Chardin, T., *Le Milieu Divin*, Collins, 1960, p. 69.
4. Joel 2:28 (R.S.V.).

> And it shall come to pass afterward,
> that I will pour out my spirit on all
>   flesh;
> your sons and daughters shall
>   prophesy,
> your old men shall dream dreams,
> and your young men shall see visions.

5. Psalm 90:10. Book of Common Prayer, 1662.

> The days of our age are three score years and ten; and though men be so strong that they come to four score years: yet is their strength then but labour and sorrow; so soon passeth it away and we are gone.

6. Harton, S., *On Growing Old*, Hodder & Stoughton, 1957, p. 89.

7. Waddell, H., *Peter Abelard*, Constable, 1936.

8. Waddell, H., *The Wandering Scholars*, Constable, 1932.

9. Harton, S., *On Growing Old*, Hodder & Stoughton, 1957, p. 74.

10. Corrigan, Dame F., *Helen Waddell*, Gollancz, 1986, p. 354.

11. St Paul's Letter to the Colossians, 1:24 (R.S.V.):

    Now I rejoice in my suffering for your sake, and in my flesh I complete what is lacking for the sake of his body, that is the Church.

12. St Paul's Letter to the Galatians, 2:2a (R.S.V.).

13. St Paul's Letter to the Corinthians, 5:1 (R.S.V.).

14. Amiel, H. F., *Amiel's Journal*, Macmillan, 1918, p. 218.

15. Vanstone, W. H., *The Stature of Waiting*, Darton, Longman & Todd (D.L.T.), 1982, p. 37.

16. St Matthew's Gospel 6:34 (A.V.).

17. Acts of the Apostles 17:28 (R.S.V.).

18. Smith, Sidney, quoted in *A Treasury of Quotations on Christian Themes*, C. E. Simcox, S.P.C.K., 1976, p. 56, No 585.

19. Clough, A. H., *Dipsychus*, Part 1, Stanza 5.

20. English Hymnal, No 503:

    Through the night of doubt and sorrow,
        Onward goes the pilgrim band
    Singing songs of expectation,
        Marching to the Promised Land.

21. à Kempis, Thomas, *The Imitation of Christ*, Revised translation, O.U.P., 1900, Book 3, Chapter XVII, paragraph 3, p. 130.

22. Book of Job 13:15 (A.V.).

23. St Matthew's Gospel 26:39 (A.V.).

24. St John's Gospel 19:30 (R.S.V.).

Chapter 3. Threats to Healthy Ageing

1. Armstrong, C., *Evelyn Underhill*, Mowbrays, 1975, p. 241.
2. ibid, p. 242–3.
3. Williams, M., private letter to Una Kroll, 1987.
4. Houghton, B., shared experience with Una Kroll, 1987.
5. Theckla, Sister, *Mother Maria*, D.L.T., 1979, p. 100.
6. ibid., p. 104.
7. ibid., pp. 113–14.
8. ibid, p. xlvii (Introduction).
9. Babington-Smith, C., *Iulia de Beausobre*, D.L.T., 1983, pp. 115–16.
10. de Beausobre, I., *The Woman Who Could not Die*, Chatto & Windus, 1938.
11. de Beausobre, I., *Creative Suffering*, Dacre Press, 1940. Now available from Fairacres Press, Fairacres, Oxford.
12. de Beausobre, I., *Flame in the Snow*, Constable, 1945.
13. Babington-Smith, C., *Iulia de Beausobre*, D.L.T., 1983, p. 104.
13. Sister Clare, S.S.C. Letter to Una Kroll, 1987.
15. Sister Mary Eleanor, S.S.C. Shared talk with Una Kroll, 1987
16. Robinson, Ruth, Letter to John Robinson's friends, 1st January 1984.

Chapter 4. Finding the Victories

1. Harton, S., *On Growing Old*, Hodder & Stoughton, 1957, p. 77.
2. Book of Job 12:12, (A.V.).
3. St Matthew's Gospel 6:34 (R.S.V.).
4. Franklin, B., *Poor Richard's Almanac* Preface, 1758.
5. St Matthew's Gospel 6:34 (A.V.).
6. Fontaine, J., *Fables*, No 6:18 17th Century.
7. Book of Acts 17:28 (R.S.V.).
8. Sister Prudence Mary, SSC. Letter to Una Kroll, 1987

9. Vanstone, W. H., *The Stature of Waiting*, D.L.T.,
    1982. P. 83.
10. ibid., p. 112.
11. Harton, S., *On Growing Old*, Hodder & Stoughton,
    1957, p. 120.
12. de Beausobre, I., *Flame in the Snow*, Constable,
    1957, pp. 147–8.
13. ibid., p. 156.
14. Eliot, T. S., *East Coker, Complete Plays and Poems*,
    Faber & Faber, 1969, p. 183.
15. Psalm 46:10. Book of Common Prayer, 1662.
16. Book of Exodus, 3:1–6 (R.S.V.).
17. First Book of Kings, 19:4–16 (R.S.V.).
18. Tournier, Paul, *The Seasons of Life.*, S.C.M. Press,
    1964, p. 23.
19. Kroll, Leopold, Private Journal, 1986.
20. St Francis of Assisi, *Oxford Book of Prayer*, ed G.
    Appleton, 1985, No 1093
21. Donne, J., Quoted in *Testament of Immortality*, ed.
    N. G., Faber & Faber, 1940, p. 243
22. Presler, H., *Helping Foreigners to Understand
    Hinduism*, 1954.
23. ibid., pp. 31–6.
24. Abishikitananda, *The Further Shore*, S.P.C.K., India,
    1975, p. 1.
25. ibid., p. 4.
26. ibid., p. 5.
27. Holy Bible: q.v. Mark 10:21; Luke 9:58–62, 14:26.
28. Morrish Ann, Poem.
29. Kroll, L., Private Journal, 1987.
30. Letter to the Hebrews 11:1 (R.S.V.).
31. Appleton, G., *Journey for a Soul*, Collins, 1976,
    p. 182.
32. St John's Gospel 19:30 (R.S.V.).
33. St Luke's Gospel 23:46 (R.S.V.).
34. St Paul's Letter to the Romans 14:7–9 (R.S.V.).
35. à Kempis, T., *The Imitation of Christ*, O.U.P, 1900.
36. Sister Jean, S.S.C. Shared experience with Una Kroll,
    1987.
37. Psalm 23:4–6. Book of Common Prayer, 1662.
38. St Paul's Letter to the Romans 8:28–39 (R.S.V.).

SELECTED BIBLIOGRAPHY

Classics

The Holy Bible.
Psalter from the Book of Common Prayer.
The Imitation of Christ, Thomas à Kempis, 1473.
Treatise on the Love of God, Francis de Sales, 1616.
Introduction to a Devout Life, Francis de Sales, 1619.
Holy Living and Holy Dying, Jeremy Taylor, 1650–51.
Holy Wisdom, the Venerable Augustine Baker, 1657.

Modern Books on Growing Older

On Growing Old, Sybil Harton, Hodder & Stoughton, 1957.
Le Milieu Divin, Teilhard de Chardin, Collins, 1960.
The Seasons of Life, Paul Tournier, S.C.M. Press, 1964.
The Noonday Devil, Bernard Basset, S. J., Burns & Oates, 1964.
The Further Shore, Abishikitananda, S.P.C.K. India, 1975.
The Stature of Waiting, W. H. Vanstone, D.L.T., 1982.

The Christian in Retirement, W. Purcell, Mowbrays,
   1982.
How to Enjoy Your Old Age, B. F. Skinner and M.
   E. Vaughan, Sheldon Press, 1983.

Modern Books on Dying and Bereavement

Healing the Dying, M. J. Linn, D. Linn and M.
   Linn, Paulist Press, 1979.
When Someone You Love is Dying, Ruth L. Kopp,
   Lion, 1980.
All in the End is Harvest, ed. A. Whitaker, D.L.T.
   Cruise, 1984.
The Five Silent Years of Corrie Ten Boom, P.
   Rosewall, Hodder & Stoughton, 1986.
Through Grief, E. Collick, D.L.T. Cruise, 1986.
Bereavement, C. Murray Parkes, Tavistock/Penguin,
   1972/1975.
Beginnings: A Book for Widows, Betty Jane Wylie,
   Unwin Paperbacks, 1982.

INDEX